G000069189

MILITARY SPACE

Brassey's Air Power: Aircraft,
Weapons Systems and Technology Series

VOLUME 10

Brassey's Air Power:

Aircraft, Weapons Systems and Technology Series

General Editor: AIR VICE MARSHAL R. A. MASON, CB, CBE, MA, RAF

This new series, consisting of eleven volumes, is aimed at the international officer cadet or junior officer and is appropriate to the student, young professional and interested amateur seeking sound basic knowledge of the technology of air forces. Each volume, written by an acknowledged expert, identifies the responsibilities and technical requirements of its subject and illustrates it with British, American, Russian, major European and Third World examples drawn from recent history and current events. The series is similar in approach to the highly successful Sea Power and Land Warfare series. Each volume, excluding the first, has self-test questions and answers.

Other titles in the series include:

Volume 1. Air Power: An Overview of Roles
        AIR VICE MARSHAL R. A. MASON, CB, CBE, MA, RAF
Volume 2. Air-to-Ground Operations
        AIR VICE MARSHAL J. R. WALKER, CBE, AFC, RAF
Volume 3. Unmanned Aircraft
        AIR CHIEF MARSHAL SIR MICHAEL ARMITAGE, KCB, CBE, RAF
Volume 4. Electronic Warfare
        AIR COMMODORE J. P. R. BROWNE, CBE, RAF
Volume 5. Air Superiority Operations
        AIR VICE MARSHAL J. R. WALKER, CBE, AFC, RAF
Volume 6. Air Transport Operations
        GROUP CAPTAIN K. CHAPMAN, M.PHIL, BA, RAF
Volume 7. Air Defence
        GROUP CAPTAIN M. B. ELSAM, FBIM, RAF
Volume 8. Strategic Offensive Air Operations
        AIR CHIEF MARSHAL SIR MICHAEL KNIGHT, KCB, AFC, FRAeS, RAF
Volume 9. Air Reconnaissance
        GROUP CAPTAIN G. OXLEE, OBE, BA, RAF

Brassey's Titles of Related Interest

C. CHANT
Air Defence Systems and Weapons: World AAA and SAM Systems in the 1990s

E. J. EVERETT-HEATH et al.
Military Helicopters

R. A. MASON
War in the Third Dimension: Essays in Contemporary Air Power

B. MYLES
Jump Jet, 2nd Edition

P. A. G. SABIN
The Future of UK Air Power

MILITARY
SPACE

Lyn Dutton, BA, MRAeS,
David de Garis,
Richard Winterton, BSc, MSc, CPhys, MInstP
and
Richard Harding, PhD, BSc, MB, BS, DAvMed, MRAeS

BRASSEY'S (UK)
(a member of the Maxwell Pergamon Publishing Corporation plc)
LONDON · OXFORD · WASHINGTON · NEW YORK · BEIJING
FRANKFURT · SÃO PAULO · SYDNEY · TOKYO · TORONTO

UK (Editorial)	Brassey's (UK) Ltd., 24 Gray's Inn Road, London WC1X 8HR, England
(Orders, all except North America)	Brassey's (UK) Ltd., Headington Hill Hall, Oxford OX3 0BW, England
USA (Editorial)	Brassey's (US) Inc., 8000 Westpark Drive, Fourth Floor, McLean, Virginia 22102, U.S.A.
(Orders, North America)	Brassey's (US) Inc., Front and Brown Streets, Riverside, New Jersey 08075, USA Tel (toll free): 800 257 5755
PEOPLE'S REPUBLIC OF CHINA	Pergamon Press, Room 4037, Qianmen Hotel, Beijing, People's Republic of China
FEDERAL REPUBLIC OF GERMANY	Pergamon Press GmbH, Hammerweg 6, D-6242 Kronberg, Federal Republic of Germany
BRAZIL	Pergamon Editora Ltda, Rua Eça de Queiros, 346, CEP 04011, Paraiso, São Paulo, Brazil
AUSTRALIA	Brassey's Australia Pty Ltd., P.O. Box 544, Potts Point, N.S.W. 2011, Australia
JAPAN	Pergamon Press, 5th Floor, Matsuoka Central Building, 1-7-1 Nishishinjuku, Shinjuku-ku, Tokyo 160, Japan
CANADA	Pergamon Press Canada Ltd., Suite No. 271, 253 College Street, Toronto, Ontario, Canada M5T 1R5

First edition 1990

Library of Congress Cataloging-in-Publication Data
Dutton, Lyn.
Military Space / Lyn Dutton, David de Maris, Richard Winterton, and Richard Harding. — 1st ed.
p. cm. — (Brassey's air power ; v. 10)
Includes bibliographical references.
1. Astronautics, Military. I. de Maris, David. II. Winterton, Richard. III. Harding, Richard M. IV. Title. V. Series.
UG1520.D87 1989 358.4—dc20 89-38723

British Library Cataloguing in Publication Data
Dutton, Lyn
Military space. — (Aircraft, weapons systems and technology series; 10)
1. Space warfare I. Title II. de Maris, David. III. Winterton, Richard IV. Harding, Richard V. Series
358'.8

ISBN 0-08-037346-1 Hardcover
ISBN 0-08-037347-X Flexicover

Printed in Great Britain by BPCC Wheatons Ltd., Exeter

Foreword

Air Commodore T. W. G. Carlton
Assistant Commandant, Royal Air Force College, 1985–88

THE TWENTIETH CENTURY has seen the face of warfare changed by the exploitation of the 'third dimension' of the skies. It is possible that it will be changed again in the twenty-first as space itself becomes the high ground to be seized and either commanded or denied to the potential adversaries. With these words Air Vice Marshal Tony Mason began his essay, 'War in the Third Dimension; Continuity, Innovation and Convergence' (Brassey's 1986). As part of a book with the same title, that essay and others became the forerunner to the Brassey's Air Power series, in which *Military Space* is published.

The idea that space-based military assets could be the decisive factor in a major confrontation has today moved from science fiction to scientific fact. Dozens of military spacecraft for surveillance, communications, weather forecasting and navigation services are on orbit and fully operational; their numbers increase on an almost daily basis. As with any other military asset their effectiveness is optimised by exercising centralised command and control. The United States has recently formed a Unified Space Command whose mission is the military control of space. They plan to achieve this in just the same way that their Navy would gain military control of the oceans. The exercise of such control in a new medium demands original thought, novel equipment and practised techniques. *Military Space* explores and explains some of the perceived mysteries of military space operations and demonstrates how classical military concepts may be extended into the 'fourth dimension'.

*　*　*

The authors of this book are members of the Royal Air Force Aerospace Briefing Team which was established in 1962 to ensure that the Royal Air Force, its sister Services, foreign military, academia, and others had a properly informed basis for studies into aerospace matters. The team, part of the Department of Air Warfare at the Royal Air Force College, Cranwell, comprises a wing commander and two squadron leaders. They are tasked with keeping all aerospace developments under continuous review and briefing as and where required. Although the team changes its members from time to time, in accordance with the normal phasing of Service postings, it has during more than 25 years developed into something of an authority on all things aerospace.

The work that the current team has produced for this book is extramural to their official duties and draws on general literature for facts on physics, chemistry, mathematics, etc. Where opinions are expressed they are entirely those of the authors and are not necessarily endorsed by the Department of Air Warfare, Cranwell, or any other UK Ministry of Defence Department.

Contents

The Future

List of Plates

List of Figures

1

Introduction

Although interest in rocketry had been expressed by the military for decades, culminating in a scramble to seize plans and technicians from Peenemunde at the end of the Second World War, the full importance of space-based assets was not appreciated until 1957. In that year, which had been designated International Geophysical Year, the Americans and Soviets had both promised to launch an artificial Earth satellite. Federal floundering frustrated the American effort and the West was stunned to hear the impudent beeps transmitted by the Soviets' Sputnik-1, launched on 4 October 1957.

The first worries expressed by the West concerned the possibility that the Soviet Union might have the technology to place a nuclear bomb in orbit around the Earth, thereby posing a tremendous threat to Western civilisation. These worries were not lessened when it was noted that the weight of Sputnik-1, some 83 kg, was considerably more than the 9-kg package which the US Navy was promising to launch on the Vanguard rocket.

The next shock came on 3 November 1957 when Sputnik-2 was launched carrying into orbit a dog named Laika, and weighing a staggering 508 kg. The fact that Sputnik-2 also carried cameras on board served to remind the military community in the United States that, earlier in the 1950s, Project Feedback had predicted that the use of satellites would herald a new era of reconnaissance.

The feeling of being left behind was heightened in the West when the long-awaited Vanguard rocket blew up two seconds after launch on 6 December 1957. The US Army finally started the Americans in the space race on 30 January 1958 by successfully launching Explorer-1 using a Jupiter rocket. Explorer-1 was a small cylinder, less than a metre long and weighing just 4.8 kg, which nevertheless provided a considerable scientific breakthrough by discovering the Van Allen radiation belts.

The first satellite to be described as a military communications satellite was launched by an Atlas rocket on 18 December 1958, although its claim is somewhat tenuous. The small satellite was called SCORE (Signal Communication by Orbiting Relay Equipment). It operated for only 13 days but became famous by transmitting a taped Christmas greeting from President Eisenhower. The military had by now, however, fully appreciated that space provided a medium ready for exploitation. This exploitation began in earnest with the launch of Discoverer-1, an ARPA (Advance Research Project Agency) mission. The launch took place on 28 February 1959, not from Florida's Cape Canaveral but the first from Vandenberg Air Force Base on the West Coast of the United States. Discoverer-1 proved that a space capsule could be orbited and then returned to Earth, thereby showing that it was possible to launch a camera on board a satellite and then return the photographs, in a capsule, to Earth. This aim was finally fulfilled when Discoverer-13 was launched on 10 August 1960. This satellite entered an elliptical orbit whose lowest point was 250 km above the Earth. Camera pods were operated when Discoverer was over the Soviet Union, and a capsule was subsequently recovered from the Pacific.

By 1961 Discoverer satellites were regularly supplying high quality photographs of the Soviet Union. The returns from the programme were enormous, as it effectively dispelled widespread US fears of a massive build-up of Soviet ICBMs (Intercontinental Ballistic Missiles). The programme also released the enormous pressures on the U-2 spy-planes, following the shooting down of Gary Powers earlier in 1960 which had demonstrated the increasing potency of Soviet SAMs (Surface-to-Air Missiles).

Since these early days, reconnaissance satellites of one form or another have accounted for over 40 per cent of all satellites launched. It can truly be said that both sides of the cold war in space have established vantage points on the new 'high ground'. However, further military advantage can be gained by denying an enemy the use of his intelligence gatherers. Consequently, almost hand-in-hand with the development of the reconnaissance satellite, there have been developments in the technology of ASAT (Anti-Satellite) weapons.

In the United States, early studies conducted in 1959 finally led to a development project for the SAINT (Satellite Interceptor). The SAINT would be launched into the same orbit as its target, inspect the victim and then destroy it. This air force project was curtailed at the end of 1962, mainly for cost reasons, and attention switched to an army project code-named Program 505. This involved adapting the Nike Zeus ABM (Anti-Ballistic Missile) for use as an anti-satellite, or ASAT, weapon. The US Air Force subsequently took a similar approach using Thor rockets, and in 1964 President Johnson announced that the United States had two operational ASAT systems, Thor and Nike Zeus.

In 1967 the Outer Space Treaty was signed. This, together with a reduction in the perceived threat from Soviet satellites, and grave doubts about the effectiveness of the ASAT systems anyway, eventually led to the abandonment of US ASAT programmes, The Soviets were a little late in the development of ASAT weapons, beginning hardware testing only in 1967. However, they persevered, and lately have caused the Americans to renew their efforts in order to avoid being left behind again. So the wheels turn full circle.

Today, military satellite technology has developed from its early, tentative attempts to exploit the new medium of space to the point where space-based systems have irreversibly superceded their ground-based counterparts in many areas. The dependence, some say over-dependence, now placed on satellites has stemmed from the fact that these space-based systems can accomplish their missions in a technically superior manner, and more economically, than could be achieved by any other means.

Satellites in orbit today can provide communication links to troops in the field, enabling them to talk directly to their heads of state or national commanders. Other satellites can provide accurate and timely information regarding the weather to be found, or expected, at any location on the Earth's surface, enabling tactics to be adapted to make the most of these weather conditions. Still other satellites allow a military commander to fix his exact location on the globe and to navigate with only a few metres of error, conferring unprecedented accuracy to his weapon systems. The military commander is also provided (detractors may prefer the word overwhelmed) with data regarding his enemy: reconnaissance satellites can not only find his position, looking beneath his camouflage, but also listen to his communications, identify and locate the radars associated with his weapon systems and much more. Meanwhile, watchful satellites keep an eye on the enemy's missile silos, ready to give warning of any escalation to nuclear war. It can truly be said that the war, hot or cold, waged upon or within the other dimensions of land, sea or air, has now spread to the fourth dimension—space.

The concept of space as another dimension in which war will be fought is a new one to many military strategists. It is only now being fully recognised as a medium which must be controlled, in much the same way as the navies of the world strive for supremacy on the oceans, air forces struggle to achieve air superiority and armies fight to secure territory. The necessity to control these other dimensions of war is obvious. Less obvious is the need to control space. To many it is still a remote region, unseen and unheeded.

The two largest nations on Earth are now coming to grips with the new concept of war in the fourth dimension, no doubt because of their large and expensive space programmes. They are formulating cohesive policies and strategies designed to enable them to gain control of space, thereby allowing their own forces free access to the new high ground, while denying access to potential adversaries, when and if required. The Americans made a great advance towards realising this aim in 1985 when the United States Space Command was formed as a unified command under the Department of Defense. Its headquarters at Peterson Air Force Base, near Colorado Springs, now serves to consolidate and integrate Department of Defense space forces into a single military organisation.

Other countries in NATO (North Atlantic Treaty Organisation) cannot hope to field forces capable of achieving control of space, even in limited areas or for limited times. Nevertheless, under the umbrella once again of the Americans, national forces are afforded some protection. Consequently, the military can rely on space assets, although no wise commander would ever rely on any asset to the exclusion of all others. Unfortunately, the full importance of space has yet to be appreciated by almost all NATO nations, and the consequent advantages of its exploitation have yet to be fully realised. Perhaps this book can help.

In keeping with the new concept of a unified approach towards space warfare, this book attempts to explain how military agencies currently use space, and will continue to use it in the future. The book is divided into sections which aim firstly to introduce the reader to the new medium of space, then to examine the various systems currently deployed by the military, and finally to show how the struggle for the control of space is being conducted.

Following this introduction is a section entitled simply Principles. The section attempts to give the reader an insight into the various constraints, both natural and man-made, which govern the way satellites behave in space. Firstly, the laws of physics which determine the orbits of satellites are explained, not with mathematical vigour but rather with a view to the practical consequences which result from their effect. Chapter 3 then describes how these orbits are reached from the launch sites around the world and the various launch vehicles and resources used by the space nations are examined. Ever since the first launches in the 1950s attempts have been made to control the military exploitation of space, consequently Chapter 4 concludes this section with a look at the various space laws and treaties which aim to limit the military use of space.

The space systems currently used by the military are examined in turn in the third section of the book. Chapter 5 considers the many satellites used to provide telecommunication links for military users. The orbits and frequencies used by these satellites are considered, followed by a more detailed look at some of the systems employed by the military. The threats posed to such vital assets are considered, and the chapter describes some of the protection techniques used to ensure jam-resistant communication links. Chapter 5 ends with a look to the future and predicts what developments are likely to take place before the end of the century.

Currently, there is considerable excitement in the military community regarding the advent of a new generation of navigation satellites. Both the Americans and the Soviets will soon be fielding constellations of satellites likely to revolutionise warfare by allowing users to pinpoint their exact locations to within a few metres. This will confer unprecedented accuracy on weapon systems and any other system requiring navigation aids. Chapter 6 looks at both the American and Soviet navigation satellite systems in detail and predicts the far-reaching impact these systems will have on warfare in the other dimensions.

Timely and accurate information regarding the weather conditions existing, and expected, in a theatre of operations enables military commanders to adapt their tactics in order to maximise the effectiveness of their forces. Meteorological satellites are an invaluable source of such information, particularly when the area to be considered is remote from home base. Chapter 7 therefore considers the wealth of data such 'Met sats' can provide and examines the systems currently employed by both East and West. Another important use of meteorological satellites is to predict when cloud-free conditions will prevail over areas of interest, thereby enabling optical surveillance satellites to be employed. The use of satellites as surveillance platforms has already been mentioned and Chapter 8 describes this application more fully. Surveillance in both the visible and infra-red parts of the electromagnetic spectrum is considered, before turning to the rather broader subject of electronic surveillance.

Some meteorological and navigation satellites fielded today by the Americans and Soviets carry receivers which listen for the distress calls of ships, aircraft and individuals. This manifestation of East–West co-operation is known as COSPAS-SARSAT, and this section concludes (Chapter 9) with a brief look at the system and how it operates.

The fourth section of the book deals with man in space (Chapter 10). Space is a dangerous medium in which to operate and this section details the constraints under which man must exist in order to survive. In particular, the physiological effects of weightlessness upon the body are far-reaching and may ultimately set a limit to what military man can achieve in the new dimension. These effects are considered in some detail, and the recent advances which have been made in overcoming them are considered.

The struggle for the control of space is then considered in the penultimate section, which begins by describing how nations keep a watch on what their possible enemies are doing in space (Chapter 11). The systems used to observe the remoteness of space and the way in which all objects in space are catalogued are examined. Chapter 12 considers the weapon systems in existence, or planned for the future, which will be used to conduct active war in space.

Finally, Chapter 13 concludes by trying to identify the trends underlying the development of space-based military systems. Identifying these trends, and considering what areas of technology are currently receiving a lot of attention, serves to indicate the direction which future developments may take. Almost inevitably, whenever predictions are made, time will prove those predictions to be inaccurate and even misleading, but it is only by looking to the future that plans can be made. It has always been so, and will also be so in space.

Principles

Principles

This first major section of *Military Space* lays the foundation on which to build your understanding of not only the remainder of the book, but also the remainder of your study of the subject.

So often one hears the question, 'Why can't we put a satellite over Moscow and . . . ?' The answer to such a question is usually complicated, because to start with one needs to give a half-hour lecture on orbital dynamics! What cannot be done in space is just as important as what can be done and therefore at the outset one should have a grasp of the basic laws of spaceflight. Consequently, Chapter 2 looks at the physical principles behind satellite orbits.

Chapter 3 then examines the practicalities of achieving those orbits. Again, if taken a step at a time, the problems and the solutions become almost self-evident. The theory is then applied to both current and future launch systems.

It is perhaps fitting that the section of this book which begins with the physical laws of spaceflight should end with the man-made laws of space, in Chapter 4. However, unlike physical laws, which cannot be broken, man-made laws or treaties are all too easy to disregard.

2

Satellite Orbits

The only practical way to maintain a military system, or indeed any satellite, close to the Earth in space is to place that system in orbit around the Earth. Satellite orbits are of various shape and size but are always very carefully chosen to allow the on-board system to perform at its best. It is therefore important that one should broadly understand orbits and the rules of space flight to gain an appreciation of the capabilities and any inherent limitations placed upon the craft by virtue of the orbital characteristics. Conversely, understanding the orbital details of a satellite is often the first step to deducing the role of that craft. There are many authoritative and exhaustive books on the subject of orbital dynamics but, perhaps surprisingly, only a broad understanding of the basic principles is really necessary to gain sufficient insight for our needs. Throughout this chapter, therefore, each principle or law will be introduced in as non-mathematical terms as possible and the emphasis will be not on the laws themselves but rather on the operational consequences of the laws.

The investigation will start by considering how the basic physical laws would relate to a satellite in orbit around an ideal, spherical, non-rotating Earth. Then, successively, the effects caused by the Earth's odd shape, its atmosphere and its rotation will be added. Finally, some of the effects caused by the small but significant influences of the Sun and the Moon will be considered.

GRAVITY

The driving force behind all orbital dynamics is the force of gravity. This fundamental and deceptively simple statement gives rise to a problem: despite the fact that everyone has experienced the effects of gravity and knows something of its effects, nobody yet properly understands the nature of the force. Gravitational laws are therefore founded on observation rather than theory.

The concrete foundation upon which our understanding must begin was laid by Isaac Newton. After about 20 years of studying and observation, in 1687 Newton published the Law of Universal Gravitation which stated:

> Every particle in the universe attracts every other particle with a force that is proportional to the product of their masses and inversely proportional to the square of the distances between the particles.

Because this force is inversely proportional to the square of the distance between two objects it follows that the closer the objects, the greater the attractive force. If

Distance apart (Earth radii)	Attractive force (Newtons)
1	15600
2	3900
5	630
10	157
15	70
20	39
30	17
40	10
60 (Moon distance)	4.4

FIG 2.1. Attractive force on a 400-kg Earth satellite.

one of the objects (or particles) is an earth satellite then the proximity of the Earth dictates that the Earth will provide by far the greatest force on the satellite compared to the sum total of forces from the Earth, Moon, Sun, planets, other satellites and every other particle in the universe. For low Earth-orbiting satellites, the Sun and Moon will have an effect but their contribution will be very small in comparison with the Earth's gravitational pull—so for the moment they will be ignored.

The practical implication of the law is that if the distance between the objects is doubled, the attractive force drops to a quarter of the previous value. To put this in perspective Figure 2.1. shows the attractive force on a 400-kg Earth satellite at various altitudes from the ideal Earth. If the table were extended beyond 60 Earth radii, the attractive force would become smaller and smaller, but it would never become zero. Indeed, at great distances other bodies may provide the primary attractive force but the attraction to the Earth will still be there, however small. Between large bodies the force will still be great even at large distances. Remember, it is just this force which keeps the Earth in orbit around the Sun, and the Moon in orbit around the Earth.

The next step is to examine how this attractive force gives rise to the familiar curved orbits.

Fig 2.2. The effect of increasing launch velocity.

ORBITS

First, imagine that somehow it has been possible to build a launch tower 200 km high at the North Pole as in Figure 2.2. If a projectile is fired horizontally from a cannon on the top of the tower, the projectile will fall to earth at point A under the effect of gravity. If the shot is repeated, but with a stronger charge, it will reach point B before it hits the ground. With a still stronger charge it will reach point C and so on, until the charge is strong enough to impart a muzzle velocity of about 7,900 m/sec when the projectile will stay parallel with the Earth's surface and return to the launch point. It will then continue to make circular orbits. The important points about circular orbits are that they are at a constant height above the Earth and the satellite has a constant speed around the orbit.

If a higher tower were used for launch, then with the correct charge a higher circular orbit would be achieved. The charge would in fact be smaller for the higher tower because a lower velocity would be needed to overcome the lower gravitational force. So the higher the orbit, the slower the orbital velocity.

Just to put some figures on the circular orbit theory, in order to stay in the very lowest orbit a satellite must be travelling at around 8 km/sec. As orbital height increases, the orbital speed decreases, rapidly at first and then more slowly. By the time we reach an orbital height of 60 Earth radii the satellite will need an orbital speed of only 1 km/sec to stay in Earth orbit. Now remember that 60 Earth radii is moon distance so it therefore should come as no surprise that the Moon moves around the Earth at about 1 km/sec.

Returning to the polar launch tower, consider what happens if the speed of launch is increased over and above that needed to achieve a circular orbit. In this case, as

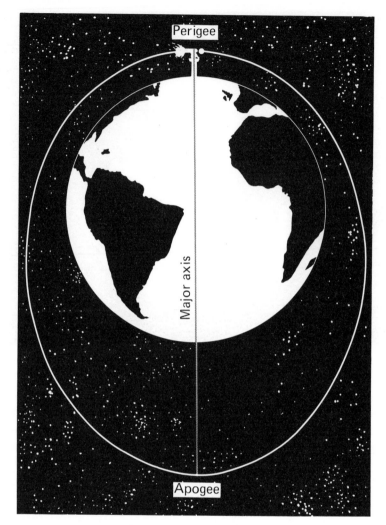

FIG 2.3. The elliptical orbit.

shown in Figure 2.3, the satellite still returns to the launch point, but only after describing an elliptical orbit. The point nearest to the Earth on this orbit is known as perigee and the point furthest from the Earth is known as apogee. The line joining these two points is known as the major axis.

If the launch speed is increased further and further, the resulting orbits are ellipses with longer and longer major axes until eventually the speed known as escape velocity is reached. This happens when the major axis is of infinite length and the body describes a parabolic path and disappears out of our area of interest. So in simple terms there are two types of closed orbit available for use, either circular or elliptical. The detailed parameters of the orbits are then carefully chosen from these to maximise the effectiveness of the payload on board a particular satellite. These orbital parameters and characteristics have to be within the limits allowed by Kepler's laws of orbital motion.

Fɪɢ 2.4. Kepler's first law.

KEPLER'S LAWS

In 1609, after eight years of studying data on the orbital position of Mars, Johannes Kepler hit on the ellipse as the shape of the orbit and he published his first two laws of planetary motion. He later published his third law in 1619. The understanding of these three laws is fundamental to all astrodynamics, so some time must be spent examining each in turn. As before, the practical consequences of each law will be stressed without attempting a rigorous analysis of it. Kepler's laws, as stated originally, dealt with the motion of the planets around the Sun. The laws are equally valid for any body orbiting around any other, so we shall relate them to Earth orbiting satellites. The laws also appear to deal only with elliptical orbits but of course a circle can be regarded as an extreme case or a simplified ellipse, so the laws are equally valid for circular orbits.

Kepler's First Law

Kepler's first law states that the orbit of a satellite is an ellipse and that one focus of the ellipse must be located at the centre of the Earth. The consequence of this law is that the plane of the orbit must pass through the centre of the Earth, as depicted in Figure 2.4.

This basic law has a practical significance on launch sites, and the orbits achievable from those sites.

Imagine that a satellite is to be launched from Cape Canaveral in Florida, in an easterly direction—this is the preferred direction of launch since it takes full advantage of the Earth's easterly spin which imparts a useful velocity to the craft while it

Fig 2.5. Launching due east from Canaveral.

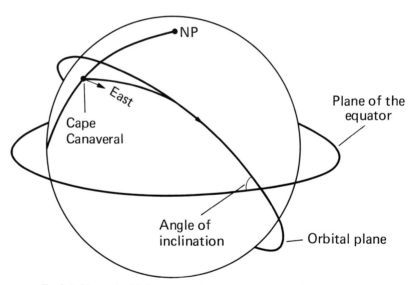

Fig 2.6. Plane of orbit for easterly launch from Canaveral.

is sitting on the launch pad. It would be tempting to assume that the ground track from such a launch would be as shown by the dashed line in Figure 2.5.

By inspection, however, it is clear that this dashed line will run all the way around the Earth at Canaveral's latitude, so the plane of that orbit would clearly not pass through the centre of the Earth as required by Kepler's first law—it is therefore impossible. In fact a satellite launched due east from Canaveral would trace out the solid orbital track shown in Figure 2.6, whose plane does pass through the centre of the Earth.

The plane of this orbit is not parallel to the equator, but is inclined at an angle.

This 'angle of inclination' is an important parameter of any orbit, and is defined as the angle between the orbital plane and the plane of the Earth's equator. By convention, it is measured anticlockwise from the equator to the orbital plane at the point where the satellite crosses, passing to the north.

If the angle of inclination for our easterly launch from Canaveral was measured, it would equal 28.5 degrees which, by more than coincidence, happens to be the value of the northerly latitude of Canaveral. By varying the direction of launch the angle of inclination can be increased from 28.5 degrees all the way up to 90 degrees and even all the way up to 151.5 degrees (180–28.5) if required, but from Canaveral it is impossible to launch directly into an orbit inclined at less than 28.5 degrees. So, therefore, as a generalisation, the minimum orbital inclination achievable is equal to the latitude of the launch site. But of course it is well known that the United States achieves equatorial orbits from Canaveral, so how do they do it?

Equatorial orbits from Canaveral are achieved by launching due east into a 'parking orbit' (inclination 28.5 degrees) and then, as the craft crosses the equator, a rocket motor is fired to effect a plane change into equatorial orbit. To achieve this manoeuvre, payload has to be sacrificed in favour of the rocket motor and the necessary amount of fuel, so this manoeuvre, though sometimes essential, costs dearly in terms of payload.

Before leaving Canaveral, it is worth considering one more direct consequence of the angle of inclination: the effect on maximum payload of changing the launch direction. Launched eastwards with the full benefit of the Earth's spin, the original Space Shuttle specification called for around 30 tonnes to be lifted into low Earth orbit at around 300 km. If, however, a polar launch is used (inclination = 90 degrees) without the benefit of the Earth's spin, the maximum payload reduces dramatically to only 19 tonnes. If the inclination is further increased to 98 degrees, which is a particularly useful orbit, a component of the Earth's spin acts in the opposite direction to launch and the maximum payload reduces even further to 14 tonnes.

So much for Canaveral, but now the plight of the Soviet Union also deserves consideration. The Soviets have two major launch sites, the most southerly of which is at Tyuratam, which has a latitude of 46.5 degrees north. The Soviet Union therefore has more difficulty in launching into equatorial orbits than the United States because the 46.5-degree plane change requires more fuel and therefore a larger vehicle than that required to carry a similar payload from Canaveral. The Soviets' second major launch site is at Plesetsk which has a latitude of 63 degrees north and, because of this fairly high latitude, the site is used for launching into highly inclined orbits.

It was previously mentioned that low inclination orbits can be achieved by reducing the inclination after launch, but a much more cost-effective solution would be to build the launch site near the equator. The French built their national launch site at Kourou in French Guiana within five degrees of the Equator, and this is the site now used by the European Space Agency for launching its Ariane series of launchers. The Italians went even closer and built the San Marco launch platform within three degrees of the equator. The San Marco platform is small, rather like an oil drilling platform, but in order to achieve an equatorial orbit, a small rocket launched

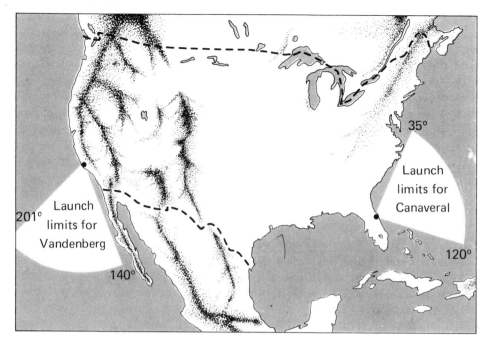

FIG 2.7. US launch direction limits.

from the equator can be just as effective as a much larger vehicle launched from high latitude.

Remarkably, all the above orbital constraints, caused by launch site latitudes, are direct consequences of Kepler's first law.

In addition to these constraints imposed by physical laws there are also severe practical constraints to be considered. The main problem which faces all launch agencies is that of expended launcher stages falling back to Earth. Most launches are designed for a fair amount of launch vehicle debris to fall back to Earth, and everyone has seen television pictures of some quite large pieces of metal being cast aside as the launch sequence progresses toward orbit. Occasionally, launches go wrong and the whole device comes down on the launch trajectory path. Clearly, this path must be over unpopulated areas if lives and property are not to be at risk. Figure 2.7 shows the US solution to the problem. Launches from Canaveral are restricted in azimuth so that the debris always falls into the ocean. For more highly inclined launches Vandenberg Air Force Base in California is used, launching towards the south so that stage debris falls into the Pacific Ocean.

The Soviet Union's problem is similar but not quite the same. Figure 2.8 shows the world map in the region of Tyuratam. Ideally, they would launch due east and this would result in an inclination of 46.5 degrees, but if they were to do so their rocket stages would fall into China. They are therefore forced to launch more to the north-east and the minimum inclination seen from a direct Tyuratam launch is around 51 degrees.

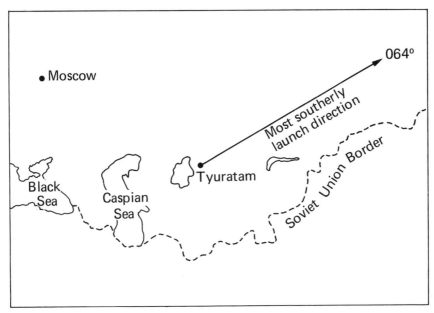

Fig 2.8. Tyuratam launch constraints.

Kepler's Second Law

Kepler's second law states that as a satellite moves around the orbit, an imaginary line joining it to the centre of the Earth sweeps out equal areas in equal times. Figure 2.9 depicts two shaded portions of the orbit area which relate to equal time periods. Clearly, the satellite must be moving around the orbit at ever-changing speeds for it to sweep out an area at the constant rate demanded by the law. An important point to note is that satellite speed is maximum at perigee and minimum at apogee. Practical use is made of this law by some surveillance and communication satellites. Surveillance satellites often have slightly elliptical orbits so they can dip down low and fast over their target area. On the other hand some communication satellites are launched into extremely elliptical orbits. As they head out to apogee, they can appear to hang almost stationary in the sky, making satellite tracking less of a problem in addition to being visible for quite long periods of time.

Kepler's Third Law

Kepler's third law deals with orbital time. It states that the square of the orbital period is proportional to the cube of the semi-major axis. In practical terms the third law means that the orbital period is dependant only on the length of the major axis—ellipticity has no effect. So if there were two orbits, one circular and one elliptical but with the same major axes, as in Figure 2.10, the orbital periods would be equal. Practically, the orbital period can be calculated if apogee and perigee heights are known.

FIG 2.9. Kepler's second law.

REAL WORLD CONSIDERATIONS

So far, only an ideal spherical Earth has been considered. It is now time to restore its natural properties and see what effects they have upon the laws considered so far.

The first problem is that the Earth is not a perfect sphere. It more closely resembles a flattened sphere, or an 'oblate spheroid' as it is more usually known. This flattening can be regarded as giving the Earth a belt of extra mass around the equator, and this extra mass gives rise to two major perturbations in satellite orbits.

Rotation of the Orbital Plane

The first of these disturbances is called rotation of the orbital plane (sometimes called nodal regression). It manifests itself as a rotation of the orbital plane about the Earth's polar axis, as depicted in Figure 2.11.

The direction of rotation is always in the opposite direction to satellite travel, so if the satellite is orbiting in an easterly direction (as they usually do), the orbital plane will rotate to the west, and vice versa. The rate of rotation of the orbital plane depends on two parameters—orbital height and inclination. Because the cause of the effect is mass-related, it follows from Newton's laws that a low-flying satellite will be more affected than one in a higher orbit. Next, a polar orbiter suffers no rotation to the orbit whereas equatorial orbits suffer the maximum effect. For the

FIG 2.10. Kepler's third law.

very lowest altitude equatorial orbits, the rate can be as high as around nine degrees per day.

At times this perturbation can be a nuisance, but it can also be used to extremely good effect in what is known as a 'Sun-synchronous' orbit.

Sun-Synchronous Orbit

Consider a satellite whose task is surveillance at optical wavelengths and whose orbital motion will bring it periodically over the same area of interest. It would be very helpful to the analysts if it could be arranged for the same sunlighting conditions from day to day as this would help them to interpret the photographs. To achieve these conditions we should have to have the sun always illuminating the orbit from the same angle. By launching into a low Earth orbit inclined at about 98 degrees, it is possible to use the orbital perturbation to rotate the orbit gradually from its preferred fixed direction in space so that over the year we compensate for the effect of the Earth's passage around the Sun. This situation is depicted in Figure 2.12.

The Sun-synchronous orbit has been used for many years by optical surveillance satellites including the US NOAA (National Oceanic and Atmospheric Adminis-

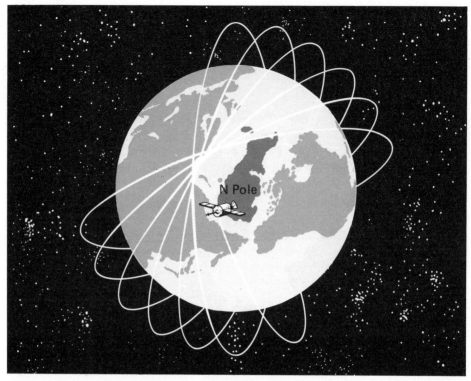

Fɪɢ 2.11. Rotation of the orbital plane.

tration) meteorological satellites, whose images are frequently seen in the news media.

Rotation of the Major Axis

The second major orbital perturbation caused by the Earth's strange shape is a rotation of the major axis (sometimes called apsidial rotation) or, alternatively, it is a movement of apogee and perigee around the orbit (see Figure 2.13). As with the previous perturbation, the rotation rate is most marked for low-flying satellites. However, in this case the direction of rotation is governed only by the angle of inclination. Rotation is maximum in one direction for polar orbits and maximum in the other direction for equatorial orbits. It follows, therefore, that at some inclination in between the rotation rate is zero, and this occurs at 63.4 degrees. So if an elliptical orbit is needed whose apogee or perigee is fixed over any particular latitude, the inclination must be chosen as 63.4 degrees. A good example of this choice are the highly elliptical Soviet Molniya communication satellites, of which more will be said in later chapters.

Other Perturbing Forces

The two major orbital perturbations already covered can cause large angular drifts in the orbital plane and the major axis, of the order of many degrees per day. Also,

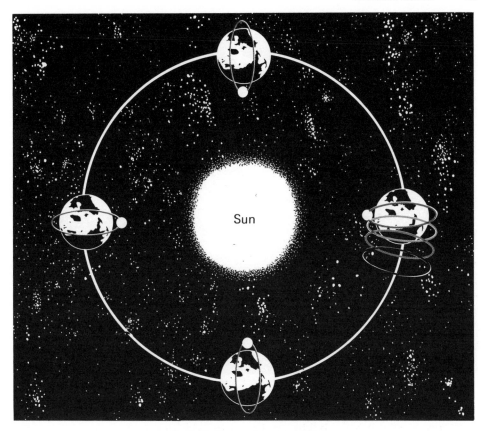

FIG 2.12. Sun-synchronous orbit.

any mass, however small, whose gravitational effect does not appear to emanate from the centre of the Earth will give rise to some disturbance on our ideal orbit. Of course, this effect will be small if the extra mass is small and very distant objects will also only have minimal effect. However, all sorts of small perturbations appear on satellite orbits and if the exact true orbital parameters are needed, the perturbing source, however small, must be accounted for. Not only will the Sun, Moon, planets, etc, give rise to perturbations, but the Earth's magnetic field will exert a pull on the ferrous parts of the spacecraft. Also, micrometeoroid impact and the solar wind will also exert a small force. These residual perturbations are small but over a long period of time could have an unwanted effect. To overcome such a problem, a rocket motor is fitted to the satellite which can be run periodically to correct the satellite's orbit as and when required.

Orbital Decay

In addition to these orbital perturbations, there is a major problem caused by the Earth's atmosphere. Even though the Earth's atmosphere is very, very thin at orbital altitude, it is still able to exert a continuous drag on the satellite which will rob it of

Fig 2.13. Rotation of the major axis.

its energy, so that it will fall into a progressively lower orbit. This gives rise to the term orbital decay, illustrated at Figure 2.14.

Atmospheric drag increases with speed and increasing air density. Both these parameters are greatest at perigee so this is where maximum drag occurs. The effect is to lower the apogee on the following orbit so that eventually the orbit becomes circularised within the denser atmosphere and then very soon the craft will suffer such kinetic heating that it will begin to burn and break up with only the larger fragments surviving to strike the Earth.

Orbital decay predictions are not very accurate, and as a rule of thumb the estimation of the time at which destruction will occur is accurate only within plus or minus 20 per cent of the time remaining to the event. For example, when a satellite is 20 days from decay, the possible prediction error is plus or minus four days. Clearly, the satellite will cover a lot of the Earth in that four days, so at the three weeks to go point, one can expect the 'It could hit Central London' type predictions in the press—and of course at that time the controllers are unable to say categorically that it won't! As the time to go shortens, so the predictions become more and more precise. Once the satellite is down to about a 110-km circular orbit it will usually impact within the next half revolution. The break-up usually occurs at about 80 km.

Further rules of thumb give the orbital lifetime of a satellite for any given altitude. Figure 2.15 gives very approximate lifetimes of some typical systems.

FIG 2.14. Orbital decay.

System	Orbital height (perigree kms)	Lifetime
Photo Recce	170	11 days
Skylab May 1973	420	6 years – impacted Western Australia, July 79
Transit	1,000	1,000 years
Skynet	35,768	1 million years

FIG 2.15. Orbital lifetimes.

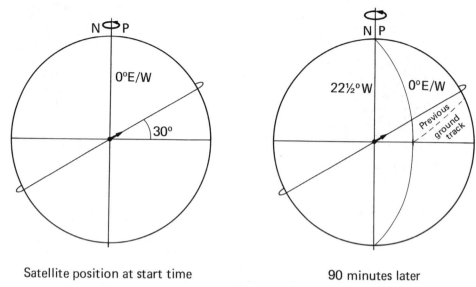

Satellite position at start time   90 minutes later

Fig 2.16. Effect of Earth rotation on satellite ground track.

Effects of Earth Rotation

So far, the perturbing effects of the atmosphere and the Earth's non-spherical shape have been considered, but next the Earth's rotation must be restored to see how that rotation influences the choice of orbit. The inter-relation between the orbit and the rotating Earth is quite difficult to visualise and is best demonstrated using rotating models. However, taken slowly it can be just as effectively described on the flat page.

First consider the very simplest of all orbits: this would be a circular orbit with zero degrees of inclination. Clearly, the ground track of such an orbit is simply the line of the Earth's equator. Next consider a circular orbit with 30 degrees of inclination, and an orbital height chosen to give an orbital period of 90 minutes. Remember that the orbital plane remains fixed in direction in space while the Earth rotates beneath it. So, with reference to Figure 2.16, assume that the satellite is already in a smooth, steady orbit. As the satellite crosses the equator on the Greenwich meridian, a stopwatch is started. Exactly 90 minutes later the satellite completes the orbit and crosses the Equator again. However, in that 90 minutes, the Earth has rotated through 22.5 degrees by virtue of the steady 15 degrees per hour easterly rotation of the planet. So the satellite crosses the Equator at its intersection with longitude 22.5 degrees west. To the observer on the Earth, who cannot sense the Earth's spin, it appears that the second orbit is passing further to his west.

Notice also that with 30 degrees of inclination, the satellite never moves further north or south of the equator than 30 degrees in latitude.

If these ground tracks build up over a period of time, successive orbits would fall further west under the influence of the Earth's spin. Because the orbital period of 90 minutes divides exactly into a day, at the end of the sixteenth orbit the satellite would again cross the Equator on the Greenwich meridian and the series of 16 ground tracks would be repeated *ad infinitum*. (In this simplified description, the

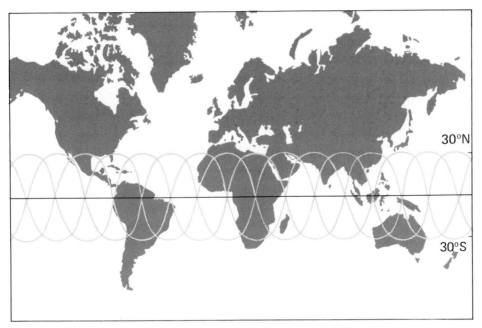

FIG 2.17. Ground tracks for a 30-degree inclined orbit.

Earth's perturbative effects on the orbit are ignored.) Figure 2.17 shows the composite plot of the build-up of the ground tracks. The plot clearly shows that the area of coverage by the satellite's sensors will be restricted to the area between 30 degrees north and south of the Equator. If the area of coverage is to be extended, the angle of inclination must be increased.

If the angle of inclination is increased to 60 degrees, the ground tracks build up as shown in Figure 2.18, again 16 tracks per day, repeated every day for a 90-minute orbiter. At 60 degrees inclination there is fairly good coverage of most of the inhabited parts of the Earth's landmass, but in military terms there are still some areas of strategic importance, particularly the arctic areas, which are outside the satellite's coverage. Again, if coverage at higher latitudes is needed, the angle of inclination must be increased further.

A point worth noting on Figures 2.17 and 2.18 is that although the plots represent one day's ground tracks, the coverage within the bounded area is not necessarily complete. That would only be the case if the swath width of the sensor carried by the satellite was equal to the gap between successive ground tracks. In our examples this swath width is large, and at the Equator it is equal to around 2,500 km, so if the satellite had a narrow swath width sensor, such as a camera, and did not have daily repeating ground tracks, it would take several days to build up full coverage.

If full world coverage is wanted, 90 degrees of inclination would be necessary, when the satellite would orbit between Earth's poles and the whole Earth would eventually be covered as it rotated beneath the satellite. But again, the time taken to achieve the full coverage would depend on ground track spacing and the swath width of the sensor on the satellite.

Next, consider the effect of the Earth's rotation on apparent orbital period.

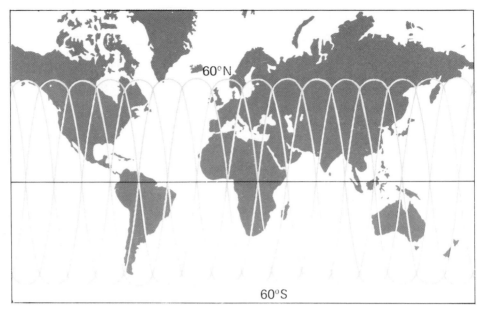

FIG 2.18. Ground tracks for a 60-degree inclined orbit.

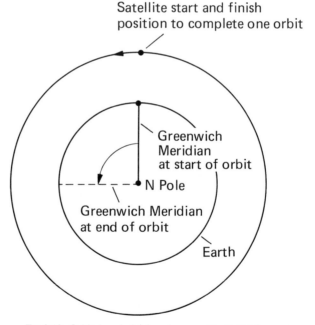

FIG 2.19. Orbital period (view down on North Pole).

Orbital period is defined as the time taken for the satellite to complete one orbit and return to the same point in space. With reference to Figure 2.19, imagine that a satellite is in a circular equatorial orbit and as it crosses the Greenwich meridian a clock is started. The orbit is complete when the satellite reaches the same point in space and not when it reaches the Greenwich meridian again. In this example, when the orbit is complete the Greenwich meridian has rotated through one quarter of a revolution so the orbital period of the satellite is one quarter of one day, or six hours. Such an orbital period would correspond to an orbital altitude of about 10,000 km.

The very shortest orbital period that a satellite can sustain is about 89 minutes. This occurs, for a satellite in a circular orbit, at an altitude of around 240 km. If the orbital period were any less, the height would have to be lower and kinetic heating from atmospheric drag would take its toll. Orbits of 88 minutes are very close to terminal decay.

As orbital height increases, so orbital period increases. If orbital height increases to 35,875 km, the orbital period of the satellite will be 1,436 minutes and the orbital period will be synchronised with the rotation rate of the Earth. Such a satellite would be called a geosynchronous satellite. Ideally, geosynchronous orbits are chosen to have zero degrees of inclination so that, to an observer on the Earth, the satellite appears to hang stationary in the sky over a point on the equator. Such a satellite would be called a geostationary satellite. These very useful geostationary points are, however, only available overhead the Earth's equator (inclination = zero) and at an orbital height of 35,875 km.

In practice all geostationary satellites' orbits have some inclination. This inclination is induced by the perturbing effects of the Sun and Moon's gravitation fields. Many satellites in such orbits therefore carry out 'north-south station keeping' to keep the residual inclination small. If unchecked, these luni-solar perturbations on a geostationary satellite would cause the orbital inclination to drift from zero, up to 15 degrees and then back to zero, over a 55-year period. If inclination is not zero, the geosynchronous satellite, as seen from the Earth, will trace out a figure-of-eight in the sky once every 24 hours. For a circular orbit, the figure-of-eight will be symmetrical about the equator and the extremities of the loops will extend in latitude north and south of the equator, by an amount equal to residual inclination, as in Figure 2.20.

In addition to north-south station keeping, the satellites have to be controlled to keep station in an east-west direction. This is because of mass concentrations in the Earth which, if ignored, would pull the geostationary satellites into one of two 'geosynchronous graveyards' which exist on the Equator at 75 degrees east and 105 degrees west.

Despite these troublesome perturbations, geostationary orbits are extremely important because a satellite in such an orbit will have a continuous, fixed view of the Earth. Similarly, the satellite user will know the fixed direction of the satellite from any location, so tracking problems are minimised. Consequently, such orbits are ideal for some types of communication and surveillance tasks.

Ground tracks of inclined elliptical geosynchronous satellites can be very complicated indeed and are beyond the scope of this book.

If the satellite is in an easterly orbit with a much greater period than the 24-hour rotation period of the Earth, the ground track will move to the west in what is known as retrograde motion. If the satellite is inclined to the Equator the orbital ground track would be something like that shown in Figure 2.21, where the track is shaped

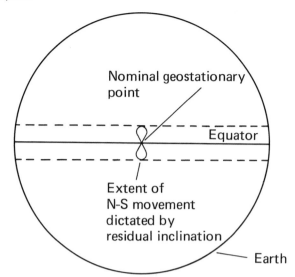

Fig 2.20. A typical ground track for a 'geostationary' satellite.

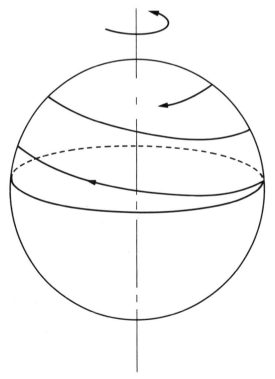

Fig 2.21. Satellite ground track for inclined orbit with period greater than 24 hours.

like a continuous spiral winding north and south between the latitidues defined by inclination. Our Moon is a good example of a satellite which exhibits these properties.

From this chapter it should be clear that there is a tremendous choice in the shape of ground tracks and of course to achieve any chosen track one simply chooses the correct orbit. The choices are wide but not infinite and all the time the constraints of the laws of orbital dynamics must be remembered.

3

Getting into Orbit

To exploit the medium of space for military, or indeed civilian purposes, it is first necessary to break loose from the bounds of earth. Contrary to the indications of Chapter 2, it has not yet become normal to launch satellites horizontally from the top of an extremely tall tower. Instead, all satellites placed in orbit to date have been launched from a vehicle which earlier had been powered from the Earth's surface by means of rocket propulsion. In the process the rocket must first have defeated the gravitational attraction of the earth and then injected its satellite into an earth orbit.

EARTH'S GRAVITATIONAL ATTRACTION

Earth's gravity varies inversely with the square of the distance from the centre of the Earth. The gravitational attraction reduces quickly with increasing altitudes when near to the Earth but that rate diminishes appreciably at greater heights. For practical purposes the value of the gravitational force is constant above about 95,000 km, reducing to zero only at 'infinity'. The concept of gravitational attraction can be conveyed by considering the Earth to be at the bottom of a deep pit whose vertical cross-section resembles that of an upturned wineglass stem. The sides are at first very steep and the vehicle must be made to climb them if it is to combat the Earth's influence. The concept is illustrated at Figure 3.1 and the reader must accept that it is three-dimensional and hollow. It can be imagined that an object fired up the side of the pit would reach a certain height on the wall before it comes to rest and reverses in direction to return to the bottom. If the initial velocity of the object is progressively increased it is clear that it will progress further and further up the sloping sides before returning to the bottom. When the initial velocity is such that the particle reaches the region where the slope shallows, very small increases in projection velocity result in large increases in distance covered. It follows, too, that there is a finite velocity which will project the object exactly to 'infinity'. That finite velocity is escape velocity, and has a value of about 11,180 m/sec. One can also appreciate that the escape velocity required from a point above the Earth's surface will be less than that from the surface.

Continuing with the concept of the pit, a number of other analogies can be made. Assuming no friction against the wall it would be possible to lift an object to a height and give it a lateral velocity so that it would ride around the wall in the same manner as Wall of Death motorcyclists at a fairground. This example is analogous to an earth satellite which has been lifted to some height within the Earth's gravitational

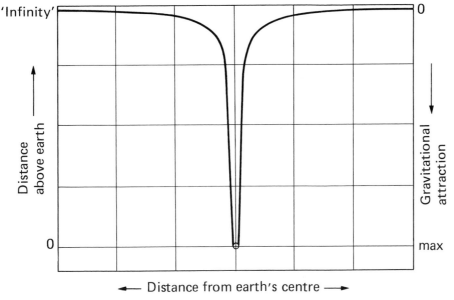

FIG 3.1. The gravitational pit.

field and given a horizontal velocity to establish it in orbit. The velocity required to keep an object at its starting height in the pit will decrease as the height of the object is increased, since the walls are always less steep with increasing height. This effect is entirely analogous to the circular orbit case described in Chapter 2, ie the greater the orbital height, the lower the circular velocity required to maintain the body in orbit. Examples of these circular velocities for a number of orbital altitudes are given at Figure 3.2.

Orbit height (km) above Earth's surface	Circular velocity (m s⁻¹)
200	7,784
500	7,613
1,000	7,350
2,000	6,898
36,000	3,066

FIG 3.2. Orbital height and circular velocity.

PRACTICAL LAUNCH CONSIDERATIONS

For simplicity, this chapter ignores the complicating factor of the variation of the Earth's gravitational field because of its non-spherical shape but even so the principles hold good in practice. Additionally, the velocity values in Figure 3.2

are only an approximation because there will be drag losses and earth rotation losses (or possibly gains). Chapter 2 informed us that an easterly launch derives a velocity increment from the Earth's rotation whereas a polar launch would derive no such benefit. The velocity increment from an easterly launch from the Equator would be of the order of 460 m/sec while a westerly launch from the same point would be penalised by the same quantity. The increment gained (or lost) would decrease with increasing latitude of the launch site until it would be zero from a Pole. Similarly, those velocity increments or decrements would reduce with launch directions other than easterly or westerly until becoming zero for a polar launch. Chapter 2 also referred to the reduction of Shuttle payload as a consequence of the launch direction effect. Nevertheless, polar orbits can provide satellite coverage unobtainable from other orbits, so the penalties of high inclination launch must be accepted. The effects of latitude of the launch site alone mean that a given payload would require a larger rocket from Cape Canaveral than the near-equatorial Kourou. An even larger rocket would be required from the Soviet launch sites which are at even higher latitudes. It is therefore reasonable to contemplate why the United States and the Soviet Union have not sought an equatorial launch site to maximise the lifting capacity of their LVs (Launch Vehicles) and to make it easier to achieve low inclination orbits. Neither has given any reason but the immense logistical problem of establishing a launch complex, the difficulty and expense of transporting rockets weighing perhaps 2,000 tonnes, and the fear for physical security of a venture supporting military goals must all be contributing factors. As it is, both nations seem prepared to build larger rockets to offset the disadvantages of high launch latitude.

Rocket propulsion is fundamental to the success of today's space programmes. In simple terms a rocket must produce a force (or thrust) to lift the weight of the vehicle and its payload and produce an accelerating force to propel that payload to the characteristic velocity required to establish it in the desired orbit. In practice vehicle selection is conducted in the reverse order by first defining the required orbit for the satellite. The orbital parameters will in turn define the required characteristic velocity. It then remains to select the LV which can generate sufficient power to propel the payload to that velocity.

ROCKET MOTORS

A rocket is basically a tube, closed at one end, containing a propellant which on combustion will produce a fast-moving exhaust flow. The rocket is attractive as an LV because of its inherent simplicity and because its weight is low compared with the high values of thrust it produces. One disadvantage is that it tends to consume its propellants extremely quickly which is to some extent offset by the very high thrust that can be generated in a short time. A rocket motor delivers a measured thrust for a finite time and the product of these two quantities describes the motor's capability. However, its efficiency will depend on the weight of propellants consumed. Thus, in the way miles per gallon describes the efficiency of a car, SI (Specific Impulse) is the engineer's measure of rocket efficiency. SI is defined as the thrust produced per unit mass of propellant consumed per second.

$$SI = \frac{Thrust}{Mass\ flow\ rate}\ \ \ Newtons\ per\ kilogram\ per\ second$$

The units can equally be expressed as metres per second. So, if a propulsion system has an SI of 3,000 Newtons/kg/sec a kilogram of fuel could give one Newton of thrust for 3,000 seconds or 3,000 Newtons of thrust for one second. Either of these burn times would give the same total change in velocity to the rocket although their accelerations would be different. A value of 2,500–3,000 Newtons/kg/sec at sea level is a typical value for most of today's rocket engines and the higher the value the more useful the vehicle. Improvements to SI require better propellants or better rocket engine design.

MASS RATIO

Mass ratio is another rocket design parameter which relates to propulsion by the mass of propellant used in the ratio of the initial (or launch) and final rocket masses.

$$Mass\ ratio = \frac{Mass\ at\ engine\ start}{Mass\ at\ fuel\ burnout}$$

Since range or terminal rocket velocity can be considered to be proportional to fuel mass, it might be assumed that scaling up a rocket to carry more fuel would be the answer to achieving greater range or velocity. However, this would require a considerable increase in mass ratio which is not readily achievable with single-stage rockets: a good single-stage rocket, regardless of size, might have a mass ratio of 10. A mass ratio for a single-stage rocket of, say, 25 would require 96 per cent of the launch weight to be fuel and this is beyond present techniques. The answer is to use multiple-stage rockets to increase performance. In this way, with conservative mass ratios for each stage, the effective mass ratio of the combination, and thus the final velocity, can be improved. For example, let us consider a 20,000-kg two-stage rocket and substitute illustrative values in the mass ratio equation above:

$$First\ stage\ mass\ ratio = \frac{Mass\ at\ engine\ start}{Mass\ at\ fuel\ burnout} = \frac{20,000\ kg}{5,000\ kg} = \frac{4}{1}$$

Following the burnout of the first stage that part of the vehicle can be jettisoned and the figures for the 2,500-kg second stage might be:

$$Second\ stage\ mass\ ratio = \frac{2,500\ kg}{500\ kg} = \frac{5}{1}$$

As the overall mass ratio of a multi-stage rocket is the product of the stage mass ratios, the advantage of staging becomes apparent. In this example the overall mass ratio is:

$$\frac{4}{1} \times \frac{5}{1} = \frac{20}{1}$$

The velocity of the multi-stage rocket after the final-stage burnout is the sum of the velocity increases from each of the stages. The increases are additive because stages start at the velocity imparted to them by the earlier stages. Thus rockets intended for interplanetary probes are likely to comprise three or four stages, each contributing its part to the high velocity requirement. By contrast, a rocket intended to place payloads into low Earth orbit does not have to generate such a high final velocity and tends to have fewer stages. If in addition the requirement is to lift large payloads into low Earth orbit, the rocket will almost certainly have 'strap-on' boosters. There may be as many as six or more of these auxiliary boosters and they are usually ignited at launch together with the main rocket engine. They have the merit of increasing the payload capability, but only incidentally the velocity gain, of their parent vehicle. Another variation is the ignition of some of these boosters at altitude where rocket efficiency is maximised in the lower density atmosphere.

PROPELLANTS

The chemical energy needed to provide the velocity to place an object into orbit can be derived from three groups of fuel types: solid, liquid or gaseous. Practically though, the low density of even compressed gas, and thus the need for a large volume of it, severely limits its applications. Fuels or propellants produce energy as a product of combustion following chemical combination with an oxidising agent. In the case of solid fuels the chemical source of oxygen is combined with the other constituents of combustion in the manufacturing process. Liquid fuels are stored separately from the oxygen source in the rocket and are mixed for combustion. Burning of the propellant produces large amounts of energy, mostly in the form of high pressure gases which when directed through the engine nozzle provide the kinetic energy to propel the rocket. Liquid fuels tend to offer higher SIs and greater control during the burning period whereas solid fuels usually provide greater stability and easier storage but, once ignited, no control over the thrust. The choice of fuel, however, is also based on practical considerations such as its toxicity, corrosive properties and cost. Many of the most efficient fuels are dangerous and difficult to handle so it is not surprising that less efficient, but more easily handled propellants are used. Indeed, many LVs originally were based on ICBMs which must be capable of being held at a high state of readiness and therefore use solid or storable liquid fuels. Solid propellants do not offer as high SI as liquid propellants—the better available solids equate only to the most basic liquid oxygen/kerosene combination. The development of solid fuelled motors has consequently lagged behind that of liquid fuelled motors so it is understandable that the former are not widely favoured for today's LVs.

Any role which needs the ability to inhibit and restart a rocket stage, eg for rendezvous, will require liquid fuel in that stage. There are two sub-divisions within the category of liquid propellants, namely cryogenic and storable. Cryogenic fuels have low boiling points and must be kept cold. Examples are liquid oxygen which boils at –182 °C (Celsius), liquid fluorine at –188 °C and liquid hydrogen at –253 °C. The low boiling points mean that these fuels must be loaded shortly before launch to avoid excessive evaporation or the necessity for prolonged refrigeration. Signs of evaporation of liquid oxygen and hydrogen fuels characterise the final preparations

PLATE 3.1. Delta Expendable Launch Vehicle with nine rocket boosters.
(*Photo: US Department of Defense*)

of every Shuttle and most other LVs of the world. Storable liquid fuels are liquids at normal temperatures and, therefore, may be stored in rockets for lengthy periods before use. Cryogenic fuels as a group produce higher SIs than their storable counterparts: the former tend to range from 250–350 m s^{-1} at sea level compared to 200–250 m s^{-1} for the latter.

LAUNCH VEHICLES

While all LVs are fundamentally similar in their principle of operation, they comprise two sub-classes: manned and unmanned. In theory the former affords greater flexibility with the ability to monitor closely the health of satellites before launch and, conceivably, retain and recover an ailing potential spacecraft. This flexibility is achieved only with the additional complexity and cost of a vehicle which meets the man-rated standards of safety in every component, including the satellites. The extra cost is offset to some degree because elements of a manned launcher are recoverable and reusable but that feature could also be built into less expensive ELVs (Expendable Launch Vehicles). The United States had intended to use exclusively the manned STS (Space Transportation System), better known as Shuttle, but by the early 1980s had realised that it would also need ELVs. By contrast, the Soviet Union has used only ELVs for its satellite launches.

Regardless of which of the two forms of LV is used, the principle of placing a satellite in orbit is precisely similar. In the initial phase of flight from lift-off, the launcher accelerates through the atmosphere in a vertical direction. Gradually, the trajectory curves over to adopt the desired launch azimuth. Lower stages will be discarded before the combination of satellite and upper stage eventually achieve a horizontal path relative to the Earth's surface. Here the remaining combination is given an injection velocity to produce a circular or elliptical orbit. Regardless of the final height of a satellite's orbit, it is usually first established in a low Earth orbit. If it is destined for high orbit, the lower level is used as a parking orbit to overcome the prohibitive consumption of chemical energy necessary to place such a satellite directly into position. A much more efficient method is the Hohmann minimum energy transfer from the parking orbit. The satellite's velocity is increased in the low Earth orbit by means of an upper stage to produce an elliptical orbit with its perigee at the injection point on the parking orbit and its apogee tangential to the desired orbit. At apogee the satellite can then be injected with a further velocity to circularise, or modify, the elliptical orbit to its final path.

Satellites can be placed into orbit with great precision. For instance, the ESA (European Space Agency) claims that the third stage of the Ariane 3 rocket launched on 28 March 1986 was accurate to within about 6 km of the 36,327-km apogee altitude specification. As the final corrections of position will be carried out using the satellite's own propulsion, this high degree of accuracy by an upper stage is valuable in conserving the satellite's fuel. Fuel is used throughout a satellite's lifetime for station keeping, so a saving of this precious commodity during the initial positioning can have a beneficial effect on its useful life. The most cost-effective method of placing a satellite into orbit is achieved by mating it with an LV of appropriate payload capability. As satellites come in a range of weights and could conceivably be placed into any of an infinite number of orbits, a wide choice of LVs would

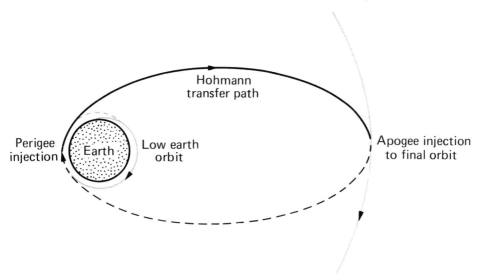

Fɪɢ 3.3. The Hohmann transfer.

be advantageous. In practice variations of performance can be achieved with a combination of differing stages, possibly using variations of fuel types, and by the addition of strap-on boosters to improve lower-stage performance. It is no surprise, therefore, that the Soviet Union which conducts approximately 100 launches per year against perhaps 30 by the rest of the world should have a greater number of LV options. The launchers of the two Superpowers are depicted at Figures 3.4 and 3.5 together with an impression of their lifting capability. Not only does the Soviet Union have a greater choice of vehicles but it also has a considerably greater overall lifting capacity (Figure 3.6). It could be argued that it needs this apparent advantage

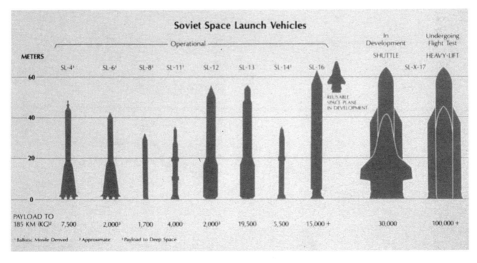

Fɪɢ. 3.4. Soviet space launch vehicles.
(*US Department of Defense*)

US Space Launch Vehicles

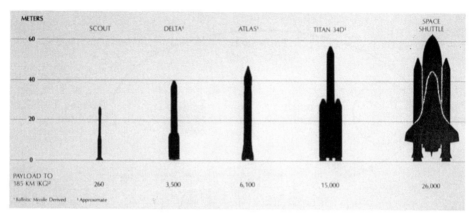

FIG. 3.5. US space launch vehicles.
(*US Department of Defense*)

US vs. Soviet Weight to Orbit

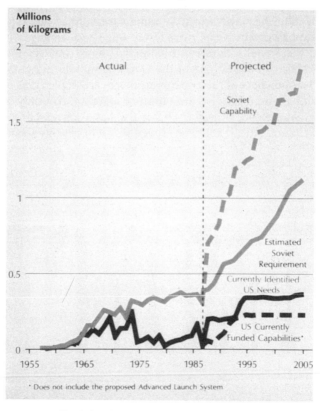

FIG 3.6. US versus Soviet weight to launch.
(*US Department of Defense*)

because its satellites are larger and heavier and are also less reliable, requiring more frequent replacement. That may be true but it has also demonstrated a much higher launch frequency over many years which would be of great military significance in placing or replacing space assets in time of tension or war. Moreover, its ability to lift heavy payloads confers a great advantage in developing large structures such as a permanently manned space station or even placing weapons in orbit. Figure 3.4 shows a space plane as a possible payload for the SL-16 launcher. Evidence for that possibility comes from photographs taken by the Royal Australian Navy of a sub-scale model being recovered from the Indian Ocean after a developmental flight in 1983 (Plate 3.2). This vehicle is too small to be manned but it is possible that when

PLATE 3.2. Soviet sub-scale space plane. (*Photo: US Department of Defense*)

the full-scale space plane is developed it could carry a crew. Figures 3.5 and 3.4 depict the US Shuttle and a similar Soviet vehicle, respectively. The latter, named Buran (Snowstorm) was launched for the first time on 15 November 1988 and completed two orbits of the Earth before landing on a runway in the central Soviet Union some 3½ hours after launch. Although Buran was unmanned for its initial flight, it is the Soviet intention to progress to manned flight and so emulate the US Shuttle. The vehicle on which it was launched is the Energiya which itself was operated for the first and only previous occasion on 15 May 1987. Energiya is currently accredited with a lift capability of 100,000 kg with development potential to 150,000 kg. The United States has no vehicle to compete with this monster since it terminated production of the 100-m high Saturn V launcher in 1970. Saturn was designed to send nearly 49,000 kg to the Moon. Two US teams of companies are now preparing designs for a new heavy-lift LV to be operational in the late 1990s. The main aim of the new vehicle is reduce the cost of launch to low Earth orbit by a factor of 10 while lifting at least 45,000 kg.

SPACE TRANSPORTATION SYSTEM

There were many exploratory programmes in the United States during the 1950s seeking to develop a means of putting man in space. By the early 1960s it had become obvious that an economical system would require two vehicles: a reusable carrier plus a form of booster to help it achieve orbit. The alternative of a totally recoverable and reusable system would have been too expensive. By 1972 considerable research culminated in a three-part configuration, the STS, being selected by NASA (National Aeronautics and Space Administration). The STS is designed to be launched as a rocket, operate as a satellite and to return to Earth as a glider. It has four elements: the orbiter we all know as Shuttle, the main tank also known as the ET (external tank), and two SRBs (solid rocket boosters). Shuttle without crew and payload weighs about 80 tonnes, a fully fuelled main tank weighs some 850 tonnes and each SRB weighs about 650 tonnes. Thus the total weight of the ensemble at launch is approximately 2,250 tonnes.

Five Shuttles were funded originally; one was built as a test vehicle and not intended for flight in space. The first orbital flight was by Columbia in 1982 and the remaining three were delivered to NASA by mid-1985. Following the tragic loss of Challenger in January 1986 agreement was reached to build a fifth orbiter at an estimated cost of $2.3bn. Each Shuttle is planned to have 100 missions and originally it was planned to conduct 26 launches per year. However, instead of achieving the necessary 14-day frequency, the first 23 flights were an average of 72 days apart and even in 1985 (the most successful year) there was still an average of 32 days between launches. Thus it can be appreciated that an earlier policy to rely on this single manned LV for deploying the great majority of US satellites was fundamentally flawed. This was recognised by the early 1980s but by that time the nation was desperately short of ELVs, an era from which it still has not emerged.

Few can be unaware that the STS is launched from a vertical position with Shuttle pointing skywards. In the launch configuration the manned vehicle and the two SRBs are connected to the main tank and each SRB is attached to the mobile launch platform by only four bolts. At launch, the three main engines which draw their liquid hydrogen and liquid oxygen fuels from the main tank are ignited first. When these have stabilised at their proper thrust level the SRBs are also ignited. Within a few seconds the combined thrust of the rockets and engines exceeds the weight of the STS and the eight retaining bolts are explosively detonated. The total thrust at lift-off is in excess of 3,000 tonnes, giving the STS a thrust to weight ratio of nearly 1.5:1, providing an unforgettable fiery sight as the combination rises into the atmosphere. The fuel in the SRBs is burnt in about two minutes and the two boosters are then jettisoned from the ET at a height of about 40 km. They descend on parachutes

PLATE 3.3. Buran in launch configuration. (*Novosti Press Agency*)

into the sea and are recovered by waiting ships for refurbishing and repacking to be used on a later launch. Meanwhile, the orbiter and ET continue to ascend for a further six minutes until the fuel is exhausted at a rate of nine tonnes a minute and the tank is jettisoned at close to orbital velocity. This tank is not recoverable and disintegrates as it enters the denser atmosphere. Thereafter adjustment to the Shuttle's final orbit is achieved by means of two OMS (Orbital Manoeuvre Systems) and would typically be conducted at about 40 minutes into flight and approximately 300 km above the Earth. A system of reaction control motors with 44 thrusters dispersed along its length is used to control vehicle attitude and to maintain the craft in its precise orbit.

Shuttle at 37 m long is similar to Concorde but, unlike the latter, it has a payload bay along its top spine. This cargo bay is a cavernous 18 m long by 4.6 m wide and is capable of housing up to four satellites. The orbiter is designed to fly in orbits up to 950 km above the Earth although the highest so far achieved is 580 km. This means that satellites destined for higher orbits must bring with them their own means of propulsion. As an example, the TDRS-C (Tracking and Data Relay Satellite) which was launched from Discovery on 29 September 1988 employed an IUS (Inertial Upper Stage) to propel it to geosynchronous orbit. This upper stage weighs more than six times that of its 2,225-kg satellite and carries more than 12,000 kg of solid

PLATE 3.4. Shuttle after launch. (*NASA*)

PLATE 3.5. Launch of the Space Shuttle. (*NASA*)

fuel propellant. In fact the IUS used two stages to place the TDRS into its required orbit and its concept of operation is identical to that of the upper stage or stages of ELVs. The TDRS is mated to the IUS and, at the appropriate position in the Shuttle's orbit, the combination is ejected from the payload bay by powerful springs. About one hour later, and when Shuttle has manoeuvred to a safe distance of over 70 km, the two-stage motor is ignited for the first of two short burns during a seven hour journey to the TDRS final orbit. There are other types of upper stage and the principle of their operation is similar. On occasions Shuttle has deployed cargoes into low Earth orbit simply by placing them clear of the payload bay by means of the extremely sophisticated Canadian-built RMA (Remote Manipulator Arm). The

PLATE 3.6. Close-up of TDRS being raised within the Shuttle payload bay prior to launch.
(*NASA*)

RMA has also been used to retrieve defective satellites from space following the space-walking adventures of astronauts.

One great difference between Shuttle and the other vehicles used for launching satellites is that it is recoverable but, of course, the recovery phase is not without its dangers. To prepare for de-orbit Shuttle is orientated tail first, then the two OMS engines are used to slow the vehicle to below orbital velocity before the reaction control motors turn it around again for re-entry. Accurate guidance is critical to ensure that the enormous kinetic energy is properly dissipated during the penetration of the atmosphere. Too low an angle and Shuttle will skip out of the atmosphere; too steep and it will burn up. The energy is dissipated by drag on the surface of the orbiter which produces temperatures of up to 2,000 °C and is insulated from the vehicle itself by silicon tiles and protective blankets. The intense heating ionises the air immediately surrounding the craft so communications with the ground are lost for about 10 minutes during the recovery phase. Everyone must have seen the later parts of the recovery of a Shuttle to a runway as a very high-speed glider and,

PLATE 3.7. Astronauts Nelson and Van Hoften repairing the Solar Maximum satellite at the aft end of the Shuttle payload bay, making use of the remote manipulator arm (from top right). (*NASA*)

PLATE 3.8. Shuttle *Challenger* landing, 6 November 1985, with a crew of eight including West German W. J. Ockels. (*NASA*)

even after more than a score of such occasions, it is still an awe-inspiring spectacle. So ends what by all accounts is an exhilarating period of up to 10 days in space but there must be underlying tension for the normal crew of seven. As it has become customary for the Shuttles to land on a long lake bed runway in California they are returned in a much more staid fashion to their launch base at Cape Canaveral on the back of a converted Boeing 747.

PLATE 3.9. Shuttle *Challenger* returning to Kennedy Space Center atop a modified Boeing 747. (*NASA*)

Originally, Shuttle was presented to the world as a civilian enterprise. The Soviets did not accept that view and for a number of years attributed it with sinister connotations. Certainly, it has been used to launch millitary satellites and at these times the normally comprehensive press releases are severely curtailed. The launch of military satellites can scarcely have been the main Soviet concern but rather the unknown or imagined military activities which might be pursued. That oft-stated concern has abated since the launch of their manned space station Mir which has maintained a virtually continuous manned presence in space since February 1986. This particular propaganda war should now end following the launch of the Soviet Buran. At a similar orbital height to Shuttle, but at a different inclination, the Mir and Buran crews could equally well conduct visual, radar and electronic surveillance and, perhaps more importantly, conduct experiments associated with ASAT (Anti Satellite) or ABM (Anti Ballistic Missile) technologies. Following the loss of Challenger and a number of losses of Titan and Atlas LVs in the last few years, Shuttle will now take on a greater military significance as the United States catches up with its launches in pursuit of 'national security'.

Man's presence in space may not be absolutely necessary with the advent of modern robotics, but quite clearly the two Superpowers believe it necessary for military purposes as well as the furtherance of scientific exploration. To that latter end all the currently significant space nations and agencies—USSR, USA, Japan, China and ESA—have plans to develop manned spaceflight. There are also West German and British concepts which could be adopted by ESA or be developed nationally.

PLATE 3.10. Artist's impression of HOTOL. (*British Aerospace plc*)

HOTOL

A British concept for a single-stage to orbit, totally reusable launch vehicle is the British Aerospace and Rolls-Royce HOTOL (Horizontal Take-off and Landing). This design exploits a conceptual breakthrough in propulsion technology which allows the vehicle to breath oxygen from the air during the early part of its flight and to convert later in flight to pure rocket propulsion. The aim is to operate it from a conventional runway and to produce an LV with very low recurring operational costs.

Much of the fuselage of HOTOL would contain fuel tanks for liquid hydrogen and liquid oxygen, the latter fuel only being used above a height of about 25 km. Between the tanks at each end of the vehicle would be a payload bay of similar diameter to that of Shuttle. HOTOL would be capable of carrying a payload of up to seven tonnes and thus could provide a launch platform for a typical geostationary communications satellite with its upper stage. It would differ from existing LVs in its mode of take-off which could be from normal airfields and from a relatively simple trolley. A lightweight undercarriage used only for landing, at about one-fifth of take-off weight, is part of the design to avoid the necessity to carry the extra weight of a robust wheel system into space. With an overall mass of about 250 tonnes it would be similar to Concorde and would require a similar take-off distance.

A typical orbital height would be 300 km with a mission length of some 50 hours. Provision is being made for manned operations but the first flights planned for the late 1990s would be remotely piloted using artificial intelligence and robotic systems. In contrast with Shuttle this vehicle would generate lower skin temperatures on re-entry, allowing the use of high temperature alloys in the construction rather than complex and expensive ceramics. HOTOL would also allow great manoeuvrability permitting it to land at an airfield in Europe from an equatorial orbit. The designers hope to reduce present launch costs of about $3,000–4,000 per kilogram to low Earth orbit by about one-fifth, and to halve the costs of reaching geostationary orbit. They also hope that with a rapid turnround capability and about 100 launches per vehicle, it could attract a large part of the commercial market for communications satellites in the twenty-first century. Although designed primarily as an LV for geostationary satellites, if the concept is proven, it could also be used to tend satellites or platforms in low Earth orbit and conceivably could have military applications.

SÄNGER

MBB (Messerschmitt-Bölkow-Blohm) of the Federal Republic of Germany has proposed an LV which would also take off from and land on normal airfields. Sänger would comprise two stages, one to be launched from the 'piggy-back' position at high level. Engine designs would not be as radical as HOTOL's but would consist of turbojet- or turbofan-ramjets on the lower stage and two conventional, but high performance, rocket engines on the upper. With the need to carry all their own fuel the combined weight of the two stages on take-off is estimated to be 340

PLATE 3.11. Artist's impression of SÄNGER. (*Messerschmitt-Bölkow-Blohm*)

tonnes (similar to a Boeing 747). The combination would climb to approximately 35 km altitude at a speed of Mach 7 before launching the upper stage. This latter stage, fuelled with liquid hydrogen and liquid oxygen, is designed to carry from two to six astronauts with a payload of two to four tonnes. An alternative unmanned cargo stage could place up to 15 tonnes into low Earth orbit. Both stages would be recovered independently to airfield surfaces. At this early stage of development MBB has claimed a reduction of launch costs by a factor of 10, half of HOTOL's. However, Europe may not be able to afford to develop both these concepts and there has been a suggestion that the two nations might unite later to pursue the more promising of the two.

OTHER MANNED VEHICLES

The ESA has plans for its own manned spacecraft. The Hermes, looking like a small Shuttle, should have its first launch in late 1996 atop an Ariane 5 expendable launch vehicle. Originally intended to be able to service the future European, US or Soviet manned space stations and satellites in low Earth orbit, it has run into growth problems. As a result the crew is reduced from six to three, its payload is reduced from 4½ to 3 tonnes and it loses the payload bay door facility. Thus the vehicle will no longer be able to launch satellites and will become little more than a taxi to elements of the Western space station to be launched in the late 1990s. The ESA is a decidedly civilian organisation but the Hermes principle could be used for military purposes. China and Japan also have plans to launch spaceplanes or manned vehicles late in this century but few details are available other than that at present they are intended for scientific use.

OTHER SPACE VEHICLES

Like Shuttle, all other manned vehicle and spaceplane concepts are designed for low Earth orbit. Their main uses are, or would be, to launch, repair and maintain satellites, provide crew and cargo transport and conceivably carry out military reconnaissance and targeting missions. In time of tension or war these craft could be used for a more aggressive, perhaps ASAT, role. However, their main drawbacks are their low orbits and their limited ability to change orbit. For instance, expenditure of the Shuttle's whole orbital fuel load could only effect a 10 degree plane change. One solution might be the provision of an intermediate vehicle. TRW Space and Technology Group of the United States has an OMV (Orbital Manoeuvring Vehicle) concept to provide just this type of link between Shuttle and other orbiting craft. With a planned range of over 2,000 km the OMV is intended to deliver, retrieve, re-boost, and service and repair satellites beyond the reach of Shuttle. The OMV itself could be recovered to Earth by Shuttle for replenishment and maintenance. This device does not offer an answer to the care of satellites in the higher orbits but the principle might be extended and prove more economic than either abandoning those satellites on failure, or providing each of them with the means of autonomous recovery to a lower orbit for attention.

For manoeuvring or transfer vehicles to be effective they must be capable of achieving rendezvous with other orbiting craft. The reader will appreciate that launching a satellite in the first instance is not simply a matter of placing it at a spot in the sky. Even geostationary satellites which appear stationary to an earthbound observer have their own dynamics. Complex calculations are employed to determine the path a satellite and its LV must describe to make good a position relative to Earth from which the satellite begins its orbital life. The principle of rendezvous, or interception, between two space objects is precisely similar to that placement except that in this case not only does the rendezvous or intercepting craft have to achieve a particular orbit, it must do so at a precise instant when the other craft is at the same point on that orbit. This simple description disguises the complex mathematics but we are all aware that rendezvous and precise orbital positioning has become a frequent occurrence in spaceflight.

PLATE 3.12. Artist's impression of an Orbital Manoeuvring Vehicle (OMV) retrieving a failed communication satellite to the Shuttle. (*TRW Inc*)

COST AND RELIABILITY

Costs for launch of military payloads are not usually made available to the public and when figures are quoted it is difficult to determine the real meaning of the cost. Similarly, a quoted commercial cost may not reflect a true value but merely reflect a desire by the launch operator to establish a foothold in the market-place. This latter motive could be attributed to the Chinese and Soviets with their offers of launches, presumably to geostationary orbit, with their Long March and Proton (civilian version of SL-12) launchers for $30m. This contrasts with reported figures of $50–80m for a similar service by other launch agencies. Even though this latter figure includes Shuttle launches, the vehicle development costs must surely have been ignored for if they were included it is believed that the cost would be at least doubled.

It would be too much to expect that LVs could have faultless performance. Even the designers of Shuttle anticipated an accident for every 100 launches despite the rigorous quality control in manufacture and high safety standards. Predicted

ELV reliability is slightly lower, and those of the two major military nations have achieved between 93 per cent and 97 per cent success, with the Soviet systems generally a little more reliable. The latter's relatively better performance could be attributed to the greater familiarity with their rockets with much more frequent use. However, while fallibility remains, and the costs of satellites range from $50m to $250m and upwards, the exploitation of space for civilian and military purposes will never be inexpensive.

4

Space Treaties

The potential for the military use of space was evident from the launch of the Sputnik satellite by the Soviet Union in 1957. The possibilities were so far-reaching that a number of nations moved quickly to limit the militarisation of space, or at least inhibit what they regarded as the more aggressive use of it. Many believe that all military activity in space should be banned but they ignore the practical difficulties and even the sensibility of such action. In the first instance, the true purpose and capability of a satellite can only be confirmed by the launching nation which could no doubt be less than truthful. In any case, should military communications satellites which pose no direct threat be outlawed when their commercial counterparts can have broadly similar capabilities? Additionally, although military surveillance satellites are used in a military intelligence gathering role, they also allow their owners to guard against strategic surprise by a would-be adversary and therefore can be considered stabilising influences. Thus these decidedly military spacecraft can contribute to international peace and stability.

Whether we like it or not space has become another military arena and a number of treaties and agreements have been spawned to regulate its use. However it is difficult to determine whether they have markedly restrained the military use of space. A cynic might claim that, as with all agreements on weapons, a nation is usually willing to agree to 'restraint' when it has no intention of progressing in that particular direction anyway. Moreover, assent is certain if an accord would nullify a potential adversary's perceived advantage or prevent him gaining such an advantage. Less cynically, it might be argued that the treaties now in existence have improved international understanding without which global security would be even more fragile.

LIMITED TEST BAN TREATY

The Limited Test Ban Treaty is perhaps the first agreement, signed by the USA, USSR and UK, which is relevant in the context of this volume. It came into force in 1963 and, among other measures, bans nuclear weapon tests in the atmosphere, in outer space and under water. The United States conducted tests in space in 1962 but there are no known explosions by the signatories in that medium since the treaty was ratified. France and China, which are not signatories, conducted nuclear weapon tests in the atmosphere up to 1975 and 1980 respectively, but more recently they have confined themselves to underground detonations. The United States and Soviet Union also continue their testing underground which they justify by the need for modernisation and miniaturisation of warheads and by the requirement to check the reliability of current weapons. One result of the banning of tests in space is that knowledge of the effects of nuclear weapons on modern electronics, communications and space systems is far from complete. Many would argue that that state should prevail.

OUTER SPACE TREATY

In October 1967 the OST (Outer Space Treaty) came into force signed by the members of the United Nations at that time including both the United States and Soviet Union. More correctly it is termed the 'Treaty on Principles Governing the Activities of States in the Exploration and Use of Outer Space, Including the Moon and Other Celestial Bodies'. In keeping with the use of a diminutive of its title, the main provisions are reduced here to two main elements pertinent to our theme. First, the signatories undertake not to place in orbit any objects carrying nuclear weapons or any other weapons of mass destruction, not to install such weapons on celestial bodies or to station them in outer space in any other manner. Second, while space including the Moon and other celestial bodies is to be free for exploration and use by all states, there can be no claims of sovereignty. Moreover, those bodies are to be used exclusively for peaceful purposes with no establishment of military bases, testing of weapons or military manoeuvres.

Incidentally, the OST recognises astronauts (and cosmonauts) as 'envoys of mankind' and requires all possible assistance to be rendered in the event of accident, distress or emergency landing on the territory of another signatory followed by prompt and safe return to their homeland. Happily, this part of the treaty has not yet been invoked but there is no reason to believe that it would not be honoured. Allied to that clause is the related liability of a state for damage caused to another signatory by any object it launches into space. That liability has been invoked when, in 1979, a Soviet nuclear-powered satellite inadvertently landed in Northern Canada producing widespread contamination.

These treaties tend not to be written in precise legal terms thus allowing a great deal of individual interpretation. As an example, the phrase 'weapons of mass destruction' has variations of understanding. Nations of the NATO (North Atlantic Treaty Organisation) adhere to a definition formulated by the UN (United Nations) Security Council in 1948—'to include atomic explosive weapons, radioactive material weapons, lethal chemical and biological weapons and any developed in the future which have characteristics comparable in destructive effect'. The Soviet Union does not acknowledge that understanding but even so it uses the term in a wide range of arms control contexts. For all the debate, this potential stumbling block does not seem to have posed any significant practical problems to date. However, the advent of space weapon technologies linked to President Reagan's SDI (Strategic Defense Initiative) may change the lack of discord on the interpretation. The weapons that the United States describes as instruments of surgical precision against materials rather than men are certain to take on an entirely different mantle in the eyes of the Soviet Union. A description of the weapon technologies being researched for SDI is in Chapter 12.

STRATEGIC ARMS LIMITATIONS

An 'Agreement between the USA and the USSR on Certain Measures with Respect to the Limitation of Strategic Offensive Arms' is commonly known by the acronym SALT. SALT I was signed and ratified in 1972. Its follow-on SALT II was signed seven years later but was never ratified. The US Congress in President Carter's era declined to confer such recognition as a reaction to the Soviet invasion of Afghanistan in 1979. Nevertheless, the two parties have broadly operated within the Treaty's defined limits on strategic offensive arms. SALT II also contains provisions which have a bearing on space operations. As an example, in order to assure compliance with the treaty both sides are to use 'national technical means of verification', ie surveillance satellites, and are 'not to interfere with the national technical means of verification of the other Party'. Thus this Treaty legalises surveillance satellites and at the same time prohibits their destruction.

ANTI-BALLISTIC MISSILE TREATY

Of all the space-related treaties between the Superpowers it is the ABM Treaty which gives rise to most current debate in connection with the SDI. It is an agreement between the USA and the USSR which came into force in October 1972. The underlying principle of the treaty is that the limitation of ABM systems should provide a substantial factor in curbing the race in strategic offensive arms and thus decrease the risk of war involving nuclear weapons. At the core of the treaty is the undertaking not to deploy ABM systems in the defence of national territory. Instead each side was permitted two defensive systems, of up to 100 missiles each, to defend the national capital and also a complex containing ICBMs. Between signing and implementation, however, the treaty was limited by mutual agreement to a single system of 100 missiles to cover either the national capital or an ICBM silo complex. The Soviets chose to defend Moscow while the Americans opted for defence of missiles. The latter deployed defences around a Minuteman ICBM complex in North Dakota one day in 1976 and decommissioned them the following day. The reasons for that action have not been stated but could be attributed to high costs, limited effectiveness or even the morality of defending weapons rather than the US population. Since that withdrawal the United States has not deployed other ballistic missile defences while the Soviet Union has maintained up to 64 Galosh missiles around Moscow. It is now in the process of augmenting them with a second ring of complementary high-acceleration Gazelle interceptors, reportedly with nuclear warheads, and will probably bring the total numbers up to the 100 permitted.

Within the ABM Treaty there are numerous provisions relating to the three elements of ballistic missile defences, namely missiles, launchers and radars. Their numbers, configurations, deployment and power are all prescribed but these characteristics will not be pursued further in this volume. Instead it is useful to consider a number of other aspects which have a bearing on the research and possible eventual deployment of the SDI. First, modernisation of ABM systems is quite acceptable providing they remain land-based and at fixed sites. However, if those systems could have mobile applications on land, at sea, in the air or in space, the work should be limited to research and should stop short of the three steps of

PLATE 4.1. Artist's impression of a Gazelle missile launch. (*US DoD Photo*)

development, testing and deployment. Those provisions appear reasonably straight-forward if the conflicting understandings of 'research' by both sides are discounted. In fact, though, the matter is complicated by an Agreed Statement appended to the treaty which permits both parties to research, test and develop, but not deploy systems based on other 'physical principles'. That statement goes on to record that specific limitations for such new systems would be subject to discussion and agreement between the two sides. It is from this part of the treaty that the debate arises on the legality on continuing work on the SDI. Discussion usually centres on whether the United States is following the narrow or broad interpretation of the wording. In the view of the author the distinction is the employment, or otherwise, of new physical principles. Thus research, testing and development of systems using, for instance, laser technology is permissible, whereas deployment of laser systems would require renegotiation or withdrawal from the treaty. It remains to be seen how long the SDI research can be restrained within even the broader interpretation. That is not to suggest that the United States is flirting with the intent of the ABM Treaty any more than the Soviet Union but rather to reflect the greater public awareness of the former's activities.

ABM TREATY REVIEW

To promote the objectives of the ABM Treaty, as with most other of these major agreements, a Standby Consultative Commission was established. The purpose of this body is to consider all the questions which might arise concerning compliance ranging from resolving ambiguities; considering the effects of changes in the strategic situation; agreeing on procedures for dismantling of systems; and amending, updating and improving the treaty. While the treaty is intended to be of unlimited duration it will be reviewed at five-year intervals. However, if either side considers that the treaty acts contrary to its national sovereignty or security it has the option to with-draw its commitment with six months' notice.

OTHER SPACE TREATIES

Other space treaties designed to maintain peace and promote international stability include the International Telecommunications Convention which is intended to prevent, or at least minimise, radio frequency interference with satellites. There is also a hot-line agreement between the two Superpowers which requires them to establish and maintain two direct communication links for international crisis avoidance or crisis management purposes. This link is provided currently by Intelsat and Gorizont satellites for Washington and Moscow, respectively. Finally, to illustrate the principle of laudable intent but only superficial adherence, there is the 1975 Convention on Registration of Objects Launched into Outer Space. Curiously, neither Superpower to date has registered a launch for military purposes. If that is true, this volume belongs on the fiction shelves!

Space Systems

Space Systems

This section describes in some detail the current and proposed military payloads in space. The capabilities of the systems are formidable but one should remember that they form only part of any nation's military capability and so must be seen as an integral part of the overall military machine. Whilst reading the following chapters, consider the vulnerability of the systems in both physical and electronic warfare terms, as such vulnerability may represent a severe weakness in such a system and will therefore question its reliability in military terms.

The section is broken into Communications, Navigation, Meteorology and Surveillance, which delineate the major support roles of military spacecraft. The section ends by looking at the subject of satellite-aided search and rescue. This final section, in contrast to the other four, describes a system which requires cooperation between the United States, the Soviet Union and many other countries. It is a non-military system, although there is nothing to stop military agencies using the service. However, it does show what can be achieved by man if only suspicion and mistrust can be put to one side and the aim can be towards a shared goal.

5

Communication Satellites

Communicating with deployed forces has always presented the military commander with a problem. This is especially true in today's fast-moving world when troops may have to deploy anywhere in the world at very short notice. When compared to ordinary terrestial radio links, the communication satellite offers the military commander a number of advantages. Radio links using the VHF or UHF frequency ranges are limited to line of sight. Consequently, for long distance radio communications, the HF frequency range has been used. Using these frequencies, signals are bounced off the Earth's ionosphere, allowing the signals to reach a receiver many thousands of miles away. These HF links are subject, however, to the vagaries of the ionosphere, which causes the signals to fade and as a result HF links can sometimes be rather tenuous. By comparison, satellite communications are far more reliable. The quality of transmission is independent of the distance between the terminals and depends solely on the properties of the terminals themselves. Furthermore, the higher frequencies and wider bandwidths provided by satellites offer greater capacity to each link.

This chapter begins by considering some of the underlying principles common to all communication satellites. First, the choice of orbit is discussed and the various options explained. The frequencies used by communication satellites are then reviewed, highlighting the advantages and disadvantages associated with particular ranges. The chapter continues with a brief look at some of the military satellites in use today. There is no room to cover all the satellites used for communications but certainly the major systems are dealt with. The threats posed to such valuable assets are then considered, together with the protection methods employed. Finally, the chapter concludes with a look at the trends in communication satellite technology and a glimpse at what the future may hold.

ORBITS USED BY COMMUNICATION SATELLITES

The orbit used by most communication satellites is the geostationary orbit. As has already been described in Chapter 2, the speed of a satellite around the Earth depends only on its distance from the Earth. The further away the satellite is placed, the slower it travels. At one particular height the speed of the satellite exactly matches the rate of rotation of the Earth. If such a satellite is in a circular equatorial orbit, ie one with no inclination, it appears to remain stationary in the sky to a ground-based observer. This occurs when the satellite is approximately 36,000 km above the Earth's equator: the so-called 'geostationary orbit'.

Two main advantages are derived from placing a communication satellite in this orbit. First, as the satellite appears stationary in the sky, ground-based users do not have to track the satellite. This considerably reduces the complexity of the equipment needed by a ground terminal. Second, as predicted by Arthur C Clarke in 1945, by using three such satellites it is theoretically possible to achieve coverage of the whole world. Each satellite in geostationary orbit covers about 42.3 per cent of the Earth's surface, so by placing three satellites 120 degree apart around the geostationary orbit, every point on the Earth's surface would be in sight of at least one satellite.

In practice, however, coverage is limited to regions below latitudes 70 degree north or south. Above these latitudes the geostationary satellite has a very oblique view of the Earth's surface. Consequently, it is much more difficult to get signals into these areas owing to the increased atmospheric and ground noise caused by the long signal path through the atmosphere. In order to provide reliable communications to users in these extreme latitudes another orbit is required. The Soviet Union in particular has considerable land mass above 70 degree north and pioneered the use of a different orbit for its major satellite communication system.

The orbit used by the Soviets is known as a Molniya orbit and is highly elliptical, inclined at 63 degrees to the Earth's equator. This particular angle of inclination is chosen as it prevents the apogee and perigee wandering around the orbital plane. The perigee is only about 450 km from the Earth but the apogee is 40,000 km away. A satellite in this orbit rushes around perigee before heading away from the Earth towards apogee. Approaching apogee it slows considerably, appearing to hang in the sky as it passes through the point furthest from Earth and begins its descent back towards perigee. As it falls back towards Earth, it speeds up again, rushing through perigee and so beginning its next orbit. It is while the satellite approaches and leaves apogee that it travels most slowly and it is then that it can be used for communications. The period of the Molniya orbit is 12 hours, so each satellite in the system will climb to apogee twice a day. The first apogee is directly above the Soviet Union and the satellite can be used for about eight hours. The second apogee is actually over Canada but the satellite is so high in the sky that it can still be used for communication by the Soviet Union for about six hours. By careful positioning, a constellation of three satellites could provide 24-hour coverage, but the Soviet Union uses four satellites in each system. The Molniya orbit is shown diagramatically in Figure 5.1.

The United States is also interested in providing communication, command and control in extreme northerly latitudes, particularly for its polar nuclear forces. Consequently, the American SDS (Satellite Data System), which forms part of the (Air Force Satellite Communications) AFSATCOM programme, also uses satellites travelling in such orbits.

Both types of orbit discussed so far are used by satellites which beam their signals over a wide area of the Earth's surface. These signals, although no doubt coded when necessary, can nevertheless be picked up by an enemy. For covert communications it would help if the signals could be radiated only to the desired recipient. Antenna design is only now achieving sufficient refinement to provide such a service. In the

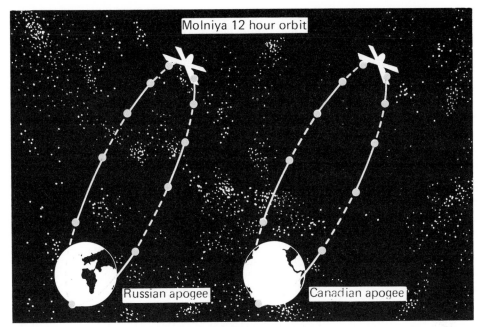

Fig 5.1. The Molniya orbit.

past the problem has been solved by using satellites orbiting at much lower altitudes, giving rise to a third type of orbit, one used primarily by covert communication satellites.

These lower altitude satellites do not have such a wide field of view as satellites in geostationary or Molniya orbit. It is unlikely that such a satellite would be within view of a remote transmitter and its home station at the same time. Therefore these satellites are provided with a means of recording the data transmitted as they pass overhead. This data is then played back as they pass overhead the receiver. This is commonly referred to as a 'store-dump' system. These satellites do not enjoy the long lifetimes of other communication satellites so they must be replaced as required. The Soviet Union, for example, launches vehicles containing either six or eight such satellites on about two occasions per year and places these into orbits inclined at about 65–70 degrees at an altitude of about 1,500 km. They appear to maintain 24 of these satellites operating in such orbits.

To summarise, these three types of orbit—geostationary, the Molniya and the low altitude orbit—are the principal ones used by communication satellites. The choice of orbit for an individual system is dictated by the type of system concerned.

FREQUENCIES USED BY COMMUNICATION SATELLITES

The frequencies used by communication satellites fall into three bands; UHF (300 MHz–3 GHz), SHF (3–30 GHz) and EHF (30–300 GHz). Each of these bands affords the user certain advantages and disadvantages, and these will be considered in some detail. The use of these frequencies must, however, be coordinated between all the users operating satellite communications. This is done by the

ITU (International Telecommunications Union), an agency of the UN. In particular, one of its organs, the International Frequency Registration Board, is responsible for coordinating the choice of frequencies and orbital locations to avoid mutual interference effects caused by using the same frequency on closely spaced satellites.

The three frequency bands will now be considered in more detail.

UHF

The beamwidth of an antenna is inversely proportional to frequency. In practical terms this means that the higher the frequency used, the narrower will be the beam-width of the radiation pattern produced. The UHF range of frequencies is the lowest used for satellite communications. Its main advantage is to allow cheap, small (man-pack size) terminals to be used. The antennas produce a wide beam of radiation, consequently tracking is a relatively simple exercise. The narrow range of frequencies available, however, means that interference could be a problem. There is also very little room in the spectrum to incorporate any anti-jamming measures.

SHF

This is the most common range of frequencies used for satellite communications. Typically, the uplink uses a frequency in the 7.9–8.4 GHz range and the down link uses a frequency in the 7.25–7.75 GHz range. The higher frequencies provide a number of very significant advantages to the user. First, as mentioned already, the higher frequency allows much narrower beamwidths to be formed, thereby increasing the satellite's EIRP (Effective Isotropic Radiated Power); in simple terms, concentrating the satellite's power over a smaller area. Furthermore, much higher capacity links can be provided, with sufficient bandwidth to incorporate some anti-jamming measures. There is always a trade-off, however, and in this case it is the low-to-moderate attenuation in the atmosphere which SHF suffers.

EHF

Typically, this is 43.5–45.5 GHz for the uplink and 20.2–21.2 GHz for the down link. The advantages of using the EHF range of frequencies are derived principally from the very much wider bandwidths available to the user. Even higher data rates and considerable anti-jamming measures can then be incorporated in EHF links. Very high gain antennas can be used, facilitating the use of steerable spot beams. The technology for use at these frequencies is still under development, however, and consequently the hardware is still expensive. This will naturally limit the use of this frequency range by military users. Another disadvantage is the high atmospheric attenuation of these frequencies, particularly by cloud and rain.

While describing the frequencies used by communication satellites, it is worth mentioning another which is destined for use by future systems. Considerable advantages accrue from the ability of various satellites in a system to talk to one another directly, passing data between themselves without having to go through a ground station. This technique will be considered in more detail later in the chapter. Suffice to say that further advantage can be gained by preventing such cross-links from being received by terminals back on Earth. The attenuation profile of the atmosphere shows a tremendous peak at 60 GHz, due to energy being absorbed by resonance of molecular oxygen. Consequently, using 60 GHz for the cross-links will go a long way to providing security for the data being passed.

CURRENTLY OPERATIONAL SYSTEMS

Having dealt so far with the underlying principles governing the use of communication satellites, some of the major systems operating today are now examined.

US Defence Satellite Communications System (DSCS)

Since the 1960s the American DSCS (pronounced Discus) satellites have provided valuable wideband communications for the US Department of Defense, State Department and other selected US Government agencies throughout the world. Currently, the system employs two types of satellite: DSCS II and DSCS III, both of which display interesting technological features, typical of their respective generations.

DSCS II. The first pair of DSCS II satellites were launched on 2 November 1971 aboard a Titan IIIC, and since then a further 13 have been launched. The operational complement normally consists of four active satellites and two in-orbit spares. Each satellite is cylindrical in shape, 3.95 metres long with a diameter of 2.75 metres and weighing 590 kg. Cylindrical satellites use spin stabilisation (60 rpm) to maintain correct orientation. The antenna system, consisting of a wide-beam horn antenna with two narrow-beam dish antennas, is de-spun and uses horizon sensors to align itself with the Earth. The solar panels used to generate power on board the satellite are wrapped around the body of the craft. Effectively, however, only about one-third of these are illuminated by the Sun at any time, limiting the amount of power supplied. A newly deployed DSCS II satellite can develop about 535 W and provide 1,300 duplex voice channels or data at 100 Mbits/sec. Plate 5.1. shows an artist's impression of a deployed DSCS II satellite.

The last DSCS II was launched in October 1982 together with the first of the newer generation DSCS III satellites. At that time the constellation consisted of seven DSCS II satellites and one DSCS III. On 4 October 1985 two more DSCS III satellites joined the constellation and the whole system should have changed completely to the newer satellites by the early 1990s.

DSCS III. Each DSCS III satellite weighs approximately 1,042 kg and has a cube-shaped body, using the more modern 'three-axis' stabilisation rather than spin. This allows the solar arrays to be mounted on wings which can be orientated constantly towards the Sun, increasing the amount of power developed; a DSCS III satellite can develop approximately 1,100 W.

Although the DSCS III satellites have similar communication capacity to their predecessors, they in fact represent a leap forward in technology when the ECCM (electronic counter-countermeasures) features provided are considered. The ante-

PLATE 5.1. The DSCS II satellite (*US DoD Photo*)

nnas consist of an advanced multi-beam lens antenna that receives on 61 separate beams and two 19-beam transmit antennas. The radiation patterns of these antennas are controlled from the ground and provide the capability to shape the patterns to match selected coverage areas and to create nulls, a powerful counter against jamming. The satellites are also hardened against nuclear radiation effects. Although such hardening cannot protect against direct attack, it is designed to withstand the SGEMP (Systems Generated Electromagnetic Pulse) effects of a nuclear explosion in space, viz X-rays and gamma rays. Another important feature of the DSCS III satellites is the design lifetime of 10 years compared with five years for the older generation II craft, thus reducing the cost of keeping the system operational. Plate 5.2 shows an artist's impression of a DSCS III satellite in orbit. The lower antenna is the receiver with the two transmit antennas above it.

Skynet

It is interesting to note that the world's first geostationary defence communication satellite was British, Skynet-1, launched in November 1969 and placed over the Indian Ocean to provide strategic communications between the UK and the Middle and Far East. Although its maximum power was only 3 W(!), it nevertheless provided 23 voice circuits or 250 telegraph channels. Skynet-1 operated for five years

PLATE 5.2. The DSCS III satellite. (*GE Astro Space*)

before being retired in 1974 and it has now drifted to the geostationary graveyard at 105 degrees west.

Skynet-1 was replaced by a second generation of spacecraft. Skynet-2A was lost on launch in early 1974, but 2B was launched successfully in November 1974. Skynet-2B is still operational today, although a command link failure has left the spacecraft out of control and wandering in the geostationary orbit between the Greenwich meridian and the Philippines.

The third generation of British communications satellites began the project definition phase in 1972, but the 1974 Defence Review saw Britain's role as a world power in decline and led to a withdrawal from bases east of Suez; Skynet-3 was cancelled.

The Royal Navy still needed satellites for worldwide communications and was forced to make increasing use of NATO and US space systems. It had become apparent by 1978, however, that a new generation of British communications satellite was required, and in 1980 the Skynet-4 programme entered the project definition phase. Production was begun by British Aerospace and Marconi in 1982. An analysis of the initial funding of £200m for the first phase of the project gives some insight to the various requirements of the services: Navy 80 per cent, Army 17 per cent, RAF 1.7 per cent and MOD (PE) 1.3 per cent.

The Skynet-4 programme is divided into two stages. The first aims to provide three satellites in geostationary orbit at locations one degree west, six degrees east and an in-orbit spare at 53 degrees east. The first of these satellites, Skynet-4A, was originally scheduled for launch aboard the Shuttle in June 1986 but the Challenger tragedy and problems with Ariane's third stage have caused considerable delays and rescheduling of the launch of the Skynet-4 system. Skynet-4B was launched in December 1988 and now fills a slot at one degree west. Communication channels were opened in February 1989, and the satellite is working well. Skynet-4A was due for launch in September 1989. with -4C following in mid-1990. The second stage of the project aims to replace the first stage satellites after they have been in orbit for five years. Two satellites are planned, referred to as Skynets-D and -E.

Each satellite weighs over 670 kg and will provide an impressive communications capability with four SHF channels (7.2–8.4 GHz), two UHF channels (250–312 MHz) and an experimental EHF receiver for research work in the 43–45 GHz band. As with the newer DSCS craft, three-axis stabilisation has been used allowing the solar arrays to be mounted on wings over six metres long. These are designed to generate over 1,300 W even at the end of seven years of operational life.

As a military communications satellite, considerable attention has been paid to the possibility that ECM (electronic countermeasure) may be used against the system and many ECCM features have been incorporated into the design of Skynet-4. An indication of some of these features is given by the complexity of the SHF aerial farm which comprises a nulling antenna and a variety of transmit antenna configurations. Four antenna coverage patterns will be used. An Earth cover beam will be of particular use to the navy, whereas a wide beam will serve the RAF and Maritime forces in the North Atlantic region. A narrow beam will serve forces in Europe and a spot beam over central Europe is designed specifically to serve small manpack and other tactical terminals, mostly in use with the army. The UHF channels are designed to serve the submarine fleet. Spread-spectrum coding techniques may be invoked, in the event of jamming being detected, to provide two highly jam-resistant 'special channels'. Spread-spectrum techniques are described later in this chapter under the heading Threats and Countermeasures. Spread-spectrum is also used to protect the TT&C (Tracking, Telemetry and Command) sub-system used to control the satellite. As with DSCS III, hardening has also been provided to protect the satellite against the radiation effects of a nuclear explosion in space. Plate 5.3 shows a Skynet-4 satellite as it will look in space. The long spiral antenna operates at UHF and the smaller, cone-shaped antenna is used to receive telemetry commands. An assortment of SHF dishes can also be seen.

Apart from the sophisticated spread-spectrum receiver, Skynet-4 satellites provide little on-board processing. The UHF, SHF, and EHF receivers act as transparent transponders, merely receiving the signals from Earth, changing their frequency, amplifying them and retransmitting them. The transponders operate linearly: the stronger the signal received, the more power is drawn from the transponder and the more power transmitted on the downlink. This would allow a powerful terminal to deny transponder power to other users and lay the system open to interference. To counter this, Skynet-4 is designed to operate under the close control of a nodal ground station, with all communication traffic passing through this point. The ground station used to control Skynet is at RAF Oakhanger in Hampshire. This vital asset will not only provide the anchor point for all communi-

PLATE 5.3. A Skynet-4 satellite (*Marconi Space Systems*)

cations to and from the satellites but will also be used to control the satellites' orbital positions and monitor the health of all the sub-systems on board the craft.

RAF Oakhanger also has separate radio equipment and aerial systems to enable it to act as a ground terminal for the US DSCS satellites over the Atlantic and Indian oceans, and the NATO satellites over the Eastern Atlantic. Due to the vital role played by the ground station, considerable attention has been paid to its protection, including a blast-wall and extensive EMP hardening. However, a fixed ground station will always be vulnerable to a certain extent, raising concern about the survivability of the system as a whole. Plans to diversify the ground control segment are already well in hand and mobile ground support units would be deployed in times of tension.

NATO Satellite Communication System

The design of the first generation of NATO communication satellites was based on the IDSCS (Initial Defence Satellite Communications System) and NATO-1 and -2 were launched on 20 March 1970 and 2 February 1971, respectively. They were designed to handle diplomatic and military communications between the United States and other NATO countries. They were placed in geostationary orbit at 18 degrees west and 26 degrees west and covered the northern hemisphere from Virginia in the United States across to Ankara in Turkey.

The next generation, which is still in use, comprised three satellites built by Ford Aerospace. These were launched between April 1976 and November 1978. Each satellite provides three SHF channels capable of handling several hundred simultaneous voice, telegraph and facsimile transmissions between ground and shipborne terminals operated by the various NATO nations. In 1980 a requirement for a fourth satellite was identified and NATO-3D was launched in November 1984. The system, funded entirely by NATO, is fully compatible with the US DSCS system.

Typical of older, spin-stabilised satellites they are cylindrical in shape, over two metres in diameter and nearly three metres long, each weighing 400 kg. The solar panels surrounding the craft's body provide 543 W of power.

Although NATO-3D is expected to provide a service well into the 1990s, plans are already under way to launch the next generation of NATO satellites. In early 1987 British Aerospace and Marconi announced that they had been awarded a contract worth $45m to build two NATO-4 satellites based on the Skynet-4 design. The launch of the first of these satellites is expected in 1990 using a McDonnel Douglas Delta-2 rocket.

Molniya

The reason behind the choice of a Molniya orbit for the major Soviet communication system has already been explained earlier in the chapter. The first satellite to be launched into such an orbit was Molniya 1-1, on 23 April 1965, and since then the Soviets have launched over 120 of this type of craft to maintain their 'Orbita' communication system. Three generations of satellites have been produced, and today's network consists of two independent systems of Molniya-1 and Molniya-3 craft. Eight Molniya-1s have apogees over central Asia and Canada (two apogees in each 24 hours). Their orbital planes are separated longitudinally in space by 45 degrees, thereby allowing the satellites to follow identical ground tracks at three-hourly intervals. The Molniya-1 constellation is thought to support mainly government and military communications. Four Molniya-3s have similar apogees, with 90 degrees of longitude between their orbital planes. A further four Molniya-3s, however, have apogees over the Pacific Ocean and the extreme eastern edge of the Atlantic Ocean, and may be associated with maritime communications.

Molniya-1 satellites each weigh approximately 1,000 kg, and are cylindrical in shape with a conical head. Six large solar arrays fan out from one end of the cylinder making the whole craft resemble a windmill. These arrays provide 500–700 W of power for the three on-board transponders. Molniya-3 satellites are larger: 4.2 metres long, 1.6 metres in diameter, weighing about 2,000 kg. Operating at higher frequencies, they are capable of relaying colour TV whereas the earlier craft had broadcast programmes mainly in black and white.

The satellites provide TV, telephone and telegraph links to approximately 100 major Orbita ground stations and over 1,000 smaller terminals, both within the Soviet Union and in other communist countries. Most Orbita stations have three Molniya-3s and five Molniya-1s in sight at any time. Until recently, Molniya-3s provided one of the two independent satellite hot-lines between Washington and Moscow, the other being provided by the Intelsat system. Recently, this role has been taken over by the Soviet geostationary system known as Gorizont, although the Molniya-3 system may still provide a back-up facility.

The technique used to place a satellite into a Molniya orbit differs considerably from that used to establish a geostationary orbit. The satellite is launched into an orbit inclined at approximately 63 degrees with a period of 700–710 minutes, rather than the 717 minutes required to stabilise the ground track (ie, to make the satellite repeat the same ground track each day). This allows the ground track pattern to drift eastwards a few degrees per day. When the correct position is reached, a small correction motor is fired, which raises the apogee, corrects the period and produces a stable ground track. There is a much reduced weight requirement for a satellite placed in a Molniya orbit as an ABM (Apogee Boost Motor) is not needed. This is an important consideration as the ABM typically accounts for between 45 and 50 per cent of vehicle weight in the transfer orbit. Further weight can be saved as a Molniya satellite requires substantially less battery power since the craft is never eclipsed within 4½ hours either side of apogee (ie, when the craft is being used).

FUTURE SYSTEMS

The systems considered so far typify the last generation of communication satellites (DSCS II) and the current generation (Skynet, DSCS III and Molniya). The next system to consider really represents the shape of things to come.

Milstar

The Milstar (Military Strategic Tactical and Relay) satellite programme was born out of President Reagan's announcement on the upgrade of strategic forces made on 2 October 1981. Scheduled for launch early in the next decade, the programme aims to provide a 'worldwide, highly jam-resistant, survivable and enduring satellite communications capability'.

The employment of countermeasures, which could be used to disrupt the use of Milstar satellites in times of crisis, has been considered in the design of this system. The use of the EHF frequency range (44 GHz uplink, 20 GHz downlink), increased on-board processing, nuclear-hardened electronic components and techniques to reduce vulnerability to laser weapons will provide considerable protection against both ECM and physical attack. Each satellite will also have direct cross-links to other satellites in the constellation, probably at 60 GHz, which will reduce dependence on ground stations. It is envisaged that by using such cross-links, a satellite could continue to operate for about six months without ground support. It is interesting to note that a similar technique is used for the Navstar programme. The ground stations themselves will be more mobile and more survivable than existing facilities. The 'worldwide' nature of the system will be achieved by placing four satellites in geostationary orbit, one of which will be a spare, and four in Molniya orbits to provide cover for high-latitude regions.

As mentioned earlier in the chapter, the use of the EHF range of frequencies provides significant anti-jam protection, and various techniques will be used by the Milstar satellites to maximise this feature. For example, an advanced antenna design will allow transmissions to be received through one of several spot beams. EHF frequencies will allow these very narrow beams to be formed using MMIC (Monolithic Microwave Integrated Circuit) solid state technology. This technique gives a capability to select a particular transmitter while excluding a jammer from the beam. The 20-GHz downlink will also employ a sophisticated antenna, capable of extremely rapid beam-hopping and spatial combination. The transmissions themselves will have spread-spectrum techniques applied to them, making them even more difficult to jam.

The use of advanced spread-spectrum coding, advanced antenna control and autonomous operation supported by satellite cross-links will lead to a requirement for the satellite to be capable of considerable amounts of on-board processing. The development of extremely powerful, yet smaller and less power-hungry computers will support this requirement.

The use of EHF frequencies will also provide considerable advantages to ground terminal equipment, particularly by allowing the use of small antenna systems capable of providing considerable EIRP (Effective Isotropic Radiated Power). For example, the US Navy is developing a 60-cm diameter antenna for its surface ships and a periscope-mounted 31-cm dish to allow communications with partially submerged submarines.

The Milstar programme is certainly the most ambitious programme yet seen in the arena of military communications satellites. It indicates the way communication satellites will develope in the future, especially with regard to the protection afforded to an otherwise vulnerable military asset. To examine further what these developments may be, it is relevant to consider what threats may be posed, both now and in the future, to communication satellites and what measures can be taken to protect these systems.

THREATS AND COUNTERMEASURES

The vulnerability of large, fixed ground stations acting as nodes in a communications network and regularly required to play an active part in the control of a communication satellite has already been mentioned. The counter to the threat thus posed is to reduce dependence on such facilities. This may be done by designing a satellite constellation to act autonomously (Milstar), or by providing considerable redundancy on the ground (Skynet). These countermeasures must be implemented before the vulnerability of the space segment can be addressed.

Although communication satellites are in many ways delicate pieces of equipment, extremely vulnerable to direct physical attack, such an attack is unlikely for several reasons. Currently, both US and Soviet anti-satellite missiles pose a threat only to low-flying satellites. Their effectiveness is limited to satellites in orbits lower than about 2,000 km whereas most communication satellites reside in geostationary orbit, 36,000 km away, out of range of present hostile systems. Weapon systems could be built, of course, to make the journey to geostationary orbit and then damage satellites in this orbit. However, such craft would be expensive, they would be unlikely to damage more than one or two satellites, and such an act would be extremely overt. Surge-launching such systems in times of hostility would also be costly and difficult. Consequently, they might instead be placed in orbit earlier to lie in wait, like mines. Once again, however, it would be difficult to sow such 'space mines' discreetly.

In view of the cost involved, the threat more likely to be faced by communication satellites will be from ECM employed against the satellite system. Such jammers could either be spaceborne, on jamming satellites, or ground-based. Jamming satellites would face two disadvantages. First, the power which a satellite can develop is limited, either by the size and efficiency of solar arrays, or by the weight penalty of taking an alternative power source into space. Second, such a jamming satellite would require agility and good positioning accuracy to get into the main beam of the target satellite. This agility would certainly limit the lifetime of such jamming satellites. In view of these difficulties, jamming is more likely to come from ground-based jammers, with much greater power resources, employing large, highly directional antennas able to deliver intense uplink jamming into the target satellite. Such jammers are likely to be based well inside enemy territory, thereby reducing the physical vulnerability of the jamming system itself.

It is clear that a jamming threat certainly exists, but to be effective an enemy must know which frequency is being used. He must then be able to generate considerable power at that frequency and deliver that power efficiently into the system. Countermeasures are required to prevent the enemy from achieving his aim. The best weapon the communications engineer has at his disposal to protect his system is the frequency spectrum itself. Spreading the transmission over as wide a range of frequencies as possible forces the jammer to spread his power to match. Two techniques can be used to do this: frequency agility, and spread-spectrum transmissions.

The principle of frequency agility is to have a number of discrete frequencies available for use. If the signal is changed between these frequencies randomly, the enemy cannot predict which frequency will be used next. To jam the transmission he must cover all the frequencies, thereby spreading out his power. The signal-to-jamming ratio is thus increased.

A more sophisticated technique is that known as spread-spectrum. Here, the signal is mixed with a highly complex coding waveform. This has the effect of spreading the power over a much wider bandwidth. A similar process carried out in the receiver unscrambles the message and concentrates the power back into a narrower bandwidth again. An enemy trying to jam the transmission must cover the total bandwidth used by the message, with considerably more power than that required to jam a conventional transmission. This is because the would-be jammer must take account of the concentration of power, back into the narrower bandwidth, which takes place in the receiver. Incredible jam immunity can be gained using this technique, at the expense of wider bandwidths. The EHF range of frequencies will allow considerable bandwidths to be made available. The spread-spectrum technique is used extensively in the Skynet system.

Other ECCM techniques rely on the use of the satellite's antennas. One such technique is to direct a special antenna solely at the jamming source. The antenna receives only the jamming, which can then be subtracted electronically from the signal plus jamming that is received by the satellite's main antenna. Other techniques use recent advances in antenna design, particularly the use of adaptive array methods, to enable nulls to be formed in the direction of any jammer—effectively excluding the jamming power from the system. This technique has been used in the DSCS III satellite system. It can be expected that the development of active arrays, using MMIC technology, will revolutionise antenna design in the future, enabling even more sophisticated ECCM techniques to be developed.

The increasing use of on-board signal processing, facilitated by smaller yet more powerful computers together with advances in antenna design, will allow extensive ECCM protection to be incorporated in future military communication satellites. Consequently, an enemy may look at other, perhaps more physical, methods of attacking these assets.

Space-based weapon systems using high intensity lasers or particle beam weapons are possibilities, and as SDI technology advances both in the East and the West, such systems may pose an increasing threat. Laser countermeasures are already being incorporated into Milstar. The deployment of such weapon systems in space, however, is governed by various treaties; the whole subject of space-based weapon systems is covered in a later chapter.

LOOK AHEAD

In the final section of this chapter, a move in technology likely to greatly influence communication satellites is examined: the use of lasers for communication links. Lasers provide two significant advantages. First, the incredibly high frequencies at which they operate allow extremely fast data transmission rates to be used. This not only allows more data to be sent over such a link but, through TDMA (Time-Division-Multiple-Access) and CDMA (Code-Division-Multiple-Access), allows many more users to be serviced by such a link. Second, lasers produce very narrow beamwidths. Typically, a laser downlink from a geostationary satellite would illuminate an area no wider than 500 metres on the Earth's surface. This would make such a link very difficult to intercept and disrupt.

The DARPA (US Defense Advanced Research Project Agency) has recently sponsored a $120m research programme looking into the practicalities of communicating with submarines, submerged at operational depths, using a laser operating at the blue wavelengths of visible light. Currently, the research programme has used airborne lasers to prove the concept but eventually the system will use satellites in geostationary orbit—the SLCSAT ('Slicksat') (Submarine Laser Communications Satellite).

SUMMARY

Modern military communication satellites are playing an increasing role in linking an ever-widening range of earthbound users. In the most recent generations of satellites quite extensive ECCM protection has been provided to protect such a vital asset. In future systems a move to the EHF range of frequencies and increased on-board processing facilities will allow even more protection to be afforded. The provision of satellite-to-satellite cross-links will also reduce dependence on fixed ground stations. In essence, it will not be easy for an enemy to deny the use of good communication links.

6

Navigation Satellites

WHY SATELLITES?

Modern large area position fixing systems are mainly radio-based systems. Powerful fixed transmitters broadcast from widely spaced land stations to give a position location service within their area of coverage. Broadly speaking, the higher the radio frequency, the greater the accuracy of the position fix. However, as the transmitters are spread further apart to give a greater area of service, so the radio frequency would have to be lowered to ensure that the radio waves 'hugged' the curvature of the Earth. By lowering the frequency, the fix accuracy would drop, and ionospheric disturbances would start to have a major effect on system accuracy. Alternatively, the radio frequency could be kept high to give good accuracy and many more transmitters could be used. However, such a system would require hundreds of costly transmitters and would still have large gaps in the coverage over ocean areas. One solution might be to put a number of navigation beacons in Earth orbit. Even a small number of such satellites could give full Earth coverage and the fix accuracy could be kept high by using the line-of-sight higher frequencies. The satellites would be moving very fast but if their precise orbital parameters were known then in principle the navigational calculations, though complex, should be straightforward for a digital computer. The navigation satellite therefore offers a possibility of providing a very accurate, global, all-weather navigation service for both military and civilian users. The remainder of this chapter will be concerned with looking at the operational navigational satellite systems working today and finish by looking towards the near future.

TRANSIT SYSTEM

In the early 1960s, when navigational satellites first became a viable proposition, the most demanding requirement for navigational information came from the US Navy's ballistic missile submarine fleet. This expanding fleet had a need for very accurate fixing data on a global basis for two main reasons. First, any error in the ballistic missiles' navigation systems on launch would be mirrored by a corresponding miss distance at the target, so the deterrent credibility of the SLBM (Submarine-Launched Ballistic Missile) force hinged on accurate navigation for the submarines. Second, the force needed a truly global navigation system so that their areas of operation would be neither limited nor predictable. The requirement led the US Navy to develop the Navy Navigation Satellite System, more commonly known as Transit. The system has been in continuous use by the US Department of Defense since 1963, and in 1967 it was made available for public use.

Navigation Fixing

The principle upon which Transit works is very simple. When listening to a Transit satellite's radio carrier frequency, there will be an apparent shift in frequency (a Doppler shift) of the signal as the satellite passes across an observer's field of view. The behaviour of the frequency shift is monitored as the satellite approaches or passes the user. The receiver then calculates its position using the measured Doppler shifts combined with the precise satellite positions which are transmitted every two minutes by the satellites. A position fix can be obtained in as little as six minutes, but more often it may take 10 minutes to get the highest accuracy. By taking Doppler measurements on one radio frequency, fix accuracies of 500 metres (95 per cent probability) are possible. The satellites in fact transmit on two frequencies and, if both are used, fix accuracies of 25 metres are possible. Navigational accuracies may in practice be degraded below these figures because the position lines calculated at two-minute intervals have to be moved to a common time to compensate for vehicle motion during the fixing cycle. To do this, the vehicle must estimate its speed during that time to calculate the distance travelled. Any error in the speed estimate will degrade the fix accuracy. A Transit receiver system is therefore usually integrated with a navigation system such as ship's log or a ship's inertial system. Also, time must be accurately known because the broadcast satellite positions are valid for an exact time. An error in knowledge of time will translate to an equivalent error in position.

Transit Orbits

Transit satellite orbits are polar and so provide world coverage. The ideal constellation would comprise four satellites, with a spacing of 45 degrees in longitude between the orbital planes. The orbits are almost circular with an altitude of around 1,100 km, which gives an orbital period of approximately 106 minutes.

With an ideally spaced constellation, satellites would not be visible at all times but the average waiting time would be between 60 and 90 minutes depending on the latitude. Unfortunately, as time goes by, the orbits slowly drift from their initial orientations because the inclinations are not exactly polar, so the gravitational perturbations described in Chapter 2 pull the orbital planes away from their ideal spacing. Consequently, there have been periods of perhaps six hours in the worst case before a satellite has been visible. Despite the drawbacks of perhaps having to wait for long periods for fixes and the need for a velocity input to the fix calculations, Transit has given excellent service, not only to the US Navy but also to around 60,000 other users worldwide, both military and civil. However, because of the previously mentioned drawbacks, Transit is really only suited to slow-moving platforms and has proved to be of little use in airborne navigation.

TSIKADA SYSTEM

The Soviet Union has had exactly the same needs as the United States for marine navigation so, not surprisingly, the Soviets have also developed navigation satellite systems. One system, Tsikada, is very similar to the US Transit system. The orbits are similar, inclined at 83 degrees to the equator at an altitude of 1,000 km with an orbital period of 105 minutes. Also, the radio frequencies used are in the same band as Transit's 150 and 400 MHz. Operational accuracy is quoted by the Soviets as 100 metres with an accurate user velocity input. Despite the similarity of the system to Transit, it has not been sold commercially in the West. On the other hand, the Soviets have bought several hundred Transit sets.

SECOND GENERATION

Systems like Transit and Tsikada represent the first generation of satellite navigation systems, giving a non-continuous service for slow-moving platforms. However, the second generation systems, which are only now just becoming operational, have overcome all the drawbacks of the first generation and are set to revolutionise navigation.

NAVSTAR GPS

In the early 1970s the US Navy was developing an advanced navigation satellite project call Timation, and at the same time the US Air Force had a similar project named 621B. In 1973 it was directed that both projects should combine under air force supervision; the combined project was to be known as Navstar Global Positioning System or, more simply, Navstar GPS. Eleven development satellites were launched between February 1978 and October 1985. These satellites performed very well and allowed extensive development work on the receiver systems. The operational satellites were then readied for launch, starting in 1986, but the Shuttle Challenger accident imposed a serious delay to the launch programme. The Delta-2 launcher was then procured, mainly to launch the GPS constellation, and after a two-year delay the first operational GPS satellite was launched in February 1989. It will take about three years to build the constellation, so the system should be fully operational by around early 1992.

Principle of Operation

The principle upon which GPS works is ranging by time difference. The satellites each carry atomic clocks, so are able to transmit an extremely accurate time signal along with the satellite's precise orbital parameters.

In essence the fixing sequence is as follows. The satellite transmits a well publicised, time-referenced, pulsed code. The receiver also generates exactly the same digital code. The two codes are generated at precisely the same time so the code received from the satellite will be late because it will take a finite time for the code to travel down from the satellite. The receiver measures the time difference between the codes. By multiplying this time by the speed of light, the user obtains his range from the satellite. If the user measured the range from three satellites, he could get a three-dimensional navigational fix, ie, his position in latitude, longitude and altitude. All this assumes that the user's clock is as accurate as the atomic clock in the satellite, but in most cases the user could afford neither the bulk nor expense of an atomic clock. The user therefore uses a cheap, small quartz oscillator clock. The error in the quartz clock can be removed by taking measurements from four satellites, using the fourth to remove time uncertainties in the quartz clock. So by taking ranges from four satellites, the user has obtained two things: his three-dimensional position and a quartz oscillator clock whose time output is as accurate as an atomic time reference. Finally, the user set calculates the user's three-dimensional velocity by a process which, in essence, uses the changes in Doppler shifts on the signals from the four satellites being used for navigation.

Control of the GPS System

The accuracy of the GPS system hinges on the accuracy of the user's knowledge of the satellites' orbital parameters and their atomic clock errors. The GPS control segment is therefore, in essence, a control loop, the function of which is to measure the orbit and clock errors as accurately as possible, then to broadcast the accurate data to the users via the GPS satellites. The control segment is described diagrammatically at Figure 6.1.

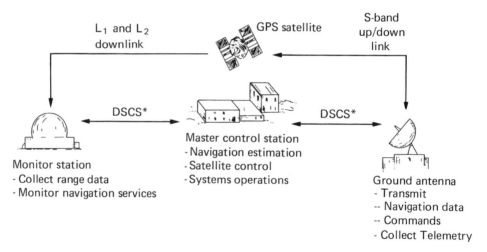

*DSCS = Defense Satellite Communication System

Fig 6.1. The GPS control segment.

Monitor stations receive the two navigation signals from each satellite and pass the data back to the Master Control Station at the Consolidated Space Operations Center at Falcon Air Force Base, Colorado Springs. The Master Control Station takes the data from each satellite and updates its estimates of each satellite's orbital parameters and clock errors. The new information is passed to the ground antennas for upload to the satellites. When each satellite receives the updates it will incorporate the new data in subsequent navigation messages, thus completing the control loop.

GPS Constellation

The basic configuration of the GPS operational constellation will initially be 21 satellites, the aim being to guarantee a minimum of 18 serviceable satellites. However, with a 21-satellite constellation there would be some small areas of the world which would have slightly degraded coverage for short periods of time because of the geometery of the constellation. For this reason, after lobbying by both Service and civilian agencies, the US Congress has now agreed that the constellation will increase to 24 satellites by the mid-1990s. The basic constellation of 21 satellites will be in six orbital planes, each inclined at 55 degrees; the full, 24-satellite, constellation will have four satellites in each of the six planes. The orbits are circular, at a height of 20,233 km which gives an orbital period of just over 12 hours. Such an orbital period dictates that each satellite's orbital plane, and therefore the whole constellation's pattern, moves one degree westwards every day. This slowly moving pattern has been chosen so that the effect of some orbital perturbations average out to zero over a complete longitudinal rotation of the constellation, so satellite station-keeping fuel is conserved.

GPS Signal

The satellite transmits its navigation message at a relatively slow rate but, in order to give the high accuracy for ranging, a much faster pulse coding is superimposed on top of the navigation message. In fact two separate codes are used which lead to two distinct levels of accuracy for the user. The coarse/acquisition or C/A code runs at around 1 MHz and is available to all: East, West, Service or civilian. Using C/A code will result in a horizontal position accuracy specified at 100 metres. On the other hand, the precision or P code runs at 10 times the rate of C/A code and gives the very highest position accuracy from the system, specified at 16 metres three-dimensional position error. In fact C/A code is inherently much more accurate than the specified 100 metres: it is more like 35 metres. However, the US authorities consider such accuracy to be of military quality, so the C/A code signal is degraded to the 100-metre accuracy level.

Because of the high military value of P code accuracy, the P code signal can be heavily encrypted to deny its use to any but the United States or those countries allowed access. Also, unlike C/A code, P code is transmitted from the satellite on two frequencies simultaneously so the effect of signal bending by the ionosphere can largely be removed, thus further improving P code positioning accuracy. In addition to the high accuracy positioning service, a GPS P code receiver will also give a velocity output accurate to around 0.1 m/sec and a time pulse accurate to 100 nanoseconds. These extremely high accuracies are available anywhere in the world, in any weather, day or night.

The highly classified encryption of the P code also makes 'spoofing' very difficult. A hostile transmitter broadcasting erroneous GPS-like data would not be encrypted properly, so would be rejected by the P code receiver.

System Performance

Although previous satellite navigation systems gave passive, worldwide perform-ance, GPS has provided several major improvements to satellite-based navigation. Fixing is continuous so there is no need to wait for several position lines to construct

PLATE 6.1. The Navstar Global Positioning System Satellite. (*USAF Photo*)

a fix. Generally, GPS receivers provide a fresh navigation fix every second. The system makes use of the WGS-84 (World Geodetic System 1984) description of the shape of the Earth and so overcomes the problem of using many different geodetic datums worldwide. Testing to date has shown that GPS equipment fitted in aircraft, ships, tanks and manpacks give accuracies well up to specification. In fact, in late 1988 the GPS Programme Office at HQ US Air Force Space Division in Los Angeles stated that the satellites' measured ranging capability was well above specification, which may lead to a P code accuracy of something closer to 10 metres rather than the 16-metre specification.

GPS Applications

GPS accuracy is so high that its use will revolutionise not only navigation but also many aspects of military operating where navigation accuracy will contribute to mission success. For example, test results have shown that using the coordinates of a target as the input to the GPS receiver resulted in bombing accuracies better than would have been obtained using aircraft radar as the input. Another, perhaps extreme example, is a receiver currently available for navigating a parachutist in his descent. The operator enters his desired landing point and follows the directions given to him on the read-out of the GPS receiver strapped to his chest. Next consider the problems of two units, say an AWACS (Airborne Warning and Control System) aircraft and an air defence ship working together. Such cooperating units have traditionally had many problems because their navigation errors have not been the same, so intruders' positions passed between AWACS and ships sometimes resulted in confusion. Since GPS errors are effectively within the wing span of an aircraft or the length of a ship, it will now be possible to correlate two detailed plots without ambiguity and confusion. The list of scenarios where GPS will benefit military operations is almost endless but only when the system has been in use for some years will the full range of possibilities become clearer.

Remember that the US Navy's ballistic missile-firing submarines' stringent navigational requirements were the original reason for navigation satellite development. It is therefore interesting to consider the effect of GPS on such systems. First, GPS will provide a very accurate and rapid fixing capability. The submariner will therefore have to expose his antenna above the sea surface less frequently than with Transit, so GPS enhances not only the navigation accuracy, but also the security of the deterrent force. Second, with a continuous accuracy of just a few metres, there is now, for the first time, the possibility of putting the fixing device inside the ballistic missile itself; indeed, the land-based Minuteman has already been test-fired with an on-board GPS navigation system. If the ICBM's accuracy can be improved, this could have a direct effect on such decisions as targeting policy and reductions in warhead size. This is another example of the far-reaching effects of such extremely high navigation accuracy.

In the commercial market there will be just as many diverse applications as in the military field. Already the market has been firmly established for merchant ships. Prototype systems for automobiles are already on the road. Airliners are being fitted with GPS/INS (Inertial Navigation) systems. And so the list grows, just as it does in the military field.

Differential GPS

Much of the error of any GPS position solution is due both to errors in the broadcast navigation message and to ionospheric and tropospheric distortion of the radio signal. These overall errors are common to any number of receivers in approximately the same area. So, if one of these receivers was placed in a well surveyed position, by subtracting the GPS-derived position from the known position, the errors could be calculated. These errors could then be transmitted so that other sets in the area could use them as corrections. The outline technique, shown at

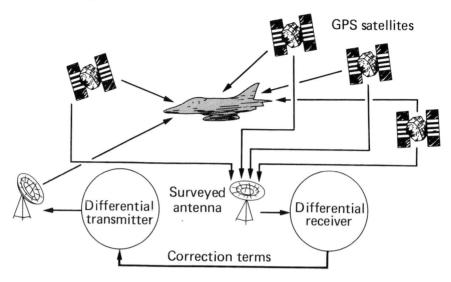

FIG 6.2. The differential GPS operating principle.

Figure 6.2, is known as DGPS (differential GPS). Today there are DGPS networks already transmitting and more are being planned. The technique will yield around four metres of position accuracy for both P or C/A (coarse/aquisition) code and the area of validity for the corrections is many hundreds of miles across. Ideally, the corrections transmitted are corrections to be added to the measured ranges from each satellite in view. Such an approach allows all the users in an area to make their corrections on any combination of satellites.

The technique is already being used in oil exploration and coastal navigation but the full military potential has yet to be explored. Those activities which will call for four-metre accuracy in the military field are few in number and very specialised, but they will no doubt be identified in time. For example, such an ability could give an air force tanker fleet the ability to take off in zero visibility conditions. Similarly, mine-hunting and -sweeping at sea could be accomplished to a previously unachievable accuracy, and therefore thoroughness.

System Vulnerability

The remarkable capabilities and the wide application of GPS make it a very attractive military target. The system's three major parts, the control segment, the satellites and the user equipment, each have different strengths and weaknesses, so the threat to each must be considered separately.

The control segment consists of the fixed monitor, control and upload stations (see Figure 6.3) which could be vulnerable to attack. However, even if the complete ground control system were destroyed, which is highly unlikely, the accuracy of fixing would degrade only slowly, so that after two weeks around 100 metres of accuracy would still be available from the P code. However, even such 'graceful degradation' is seen by the United States as a system shortcoming, so the Block-2R

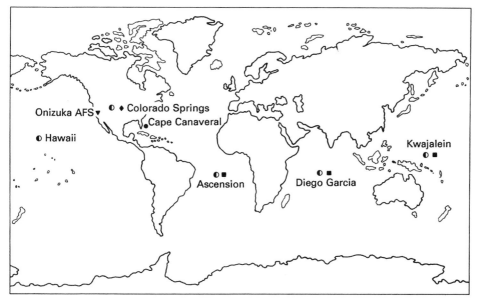

+ Master control station
▼ Planned back-up control station
◑ Monitor station
■ Ground antenna
● Prelaunch capability station
  (functional ground antenna)

FIG 6.3. Deployment of the GPS operational control system.

GPS spacecraft scheduled for launch in the mid-1990s will be capable of giving full accuracy after six months without an update from the control segment.

The satellites are invulnerable to physical attack by Soviet anti-satellites by virtue of GPS's high orbits. Also, the satellites have been hardened against electromagnetic interference. The orbits are carefully arranged so that two satellites are never close enough to be killed with one weapon. Finally, the large number of satellites gives the system a degree of redundancy if one or more were destroyed.

The greatest threat to GPS is from intense local jamming of the receivers on the Earth. However, the signals are well protected by virtue of their spread-spectrum modulation. Additionally, adaptive antennas will be widely used which will blank out directions from which jamming is detected. Many GPS systems will be integrated with inertial systems and thus the inertial will take over the navigation during those periods where jamming could be a problem.

In summary, though perhaps a prime target, the GPS system is exceptionally well protected and should provide full military accuracy to the users, even in a hostile environment.

GLONASS

The Soviet Union started launching its second generation system, Glonass, in October 1982. Since then, over 40 Glonass satellites have been launched, in batches of three, using the SL-12 launcher. Clearly, the Soviets have gone through a development phase, similar to the United States, and the declared Glonass operational constellation will also eventually have 24 active satellites, but in only three orbital planes.

Again, the Soviet system is very similar to the equivalent US system. Glonass and GPS have similar orbital altitudes, similar inclinations and operating frequencies. The mechanisation of the system is also similar in some respects, but different in others. For instance both systems have the equivalent of both a P and a C/A code. Also, the signal structures are similar. However, GPS pulse coding is twice the rate of that used by Glonass and so should theoretically lead to marginally better position accuracies. On the other hand, the Glonass ephemeris message is updated every 30 minutes and so may lead to higher accuracies than for the hourly updated GPS. In reality, however, the accuracies of the two systems should be virtually identical for all practical purposes. One significant difference between the two systems is that all GPS satellites transmit on the same two carrier frequencies and use satellite-unique codes whereas, in contrast, each Glonass satellite transmits on a unique pair of frequencies and uses common codes. The major differences between GPS and Glonass are summarised in Figure 6.4. Interestingly, Glonass's inclination would give better coverage for GPS, but the 55 degrees was imposed by the original plans to use the Shuttle for launch. Glonass's lower orbital altitude means that the satellites perform $2\frac{1}{8}$ orbits per day, so their ground track patterns repeat every eight days.

Navstar		Glonass
21 initially, becoming 24	Number of satellites	12 initially, becoming 24
6	Number of orbital planes	2 initially, becoming 3
3 initially, becoming 4	Number of satellites per plane	6 initially, becoming 8
55°	Orbital inclination	64.8°
20,233	Satellite altitude	19,100 Km
L$_1$ 1227 MHz L$_2$ 1575 MHz	Carrier Frequency	1240 - 1260 MHz 1602 - 1616 MHz
50 bits/sec	Navigation message rate	50 bits/sec

Fig 6.4. Navstar versus Glonass.

This situation is chosen, like GPS's, to average out the effects of some orbital perturbations.

Despite the few slight differences between GPS and Glonass, the similarities are such that a joint GPS/Glonass receiver must be considered a real possibility for commercial use. Such a receiver is all the more possible since the Soviet Union released full details of its C/A code signal in May 1988.

Interestingly, the Soviets have made no mention of degrading their C/A Code signal in the way that the Americans intend to do. If this were the case, the operational Glonass C/A code navigation accuracy could be much better than that available from GPS and perhaps good enough for military requirements.

Satellite lifetime is also an interesting statistic to consider. The average lifespan of each Glonass development satellite has been around four months and compares very poorly with the six years of the early GPS vehicles. For the operational constellations, GPS is designed for seven-and-a-half-year satellite lifetimes and if Glonass is to be cost-effective its satellite lifetimes will have to be much greater than at present.

THE FUTURE

It will take some time for the impact and potential of both GPS or Glonass to be fully realised. The systems will no doubt be improved and refined for some years to come. However, many lower grade satellite navigation systems have been proposed, almost exclusively for civilian purposes. Systems such as Geostar, Locstar, Starfind and Navsat are in various stages of planning or development by various agencies but, since they are essentially civil systems, they will not compete with GPS in military markets. One reason for the numerous proposed civilian systems is that the world's civil community seems reluctant to rely on GPS, which is controlled by the US military authorities and therefore could conceivably be much degraded during times of tension or war.

7

Meteorological Satellites

History books are full of examples of how weather has affected the outcome of battles. Even with modern, high technology weapon systems, the weather can still have a decisive effect on any military mission. For example, the North Vietnamese used the persistent overcast condition associated with the north-east monsoon to move men and supplies and to conduct major offensive operations with minimum exposure to American air power. A military commander can use knowledge of predicted weather to both utilise his resources to their maximum effect and to deny his enemy the full use of his assets. Consequently, timely intelligence regarding weather, properly exploited by the correct choice of tactics, can reasonably be called a force multiplier.

This chapter is concerned with the part that meteorological satellites can play in providing weather information to assist in military decision-making. In particular, such satellites are invaluable in their ability to provide high quality weather information over the whole of the Earth's surface. In times of conflict they could well be the only means of acquiring good quality weather information over areas remote from the home base. In addition, today's meteorological satellites are able to provide the military commander with a wealth of information other than conventional weather prediction. For example, they can provide information on sea surface temperatures, the position of sea fronts, the formation of ice and leads in the ice pack and the position of icebergs. This information is invaluable to the navy's surface and submarine fleets. Both land and air commanders can be provided with information regarding fog, and its formation can be predicted.

Meteorological satellites, therefore, have a lot to offer the military, and a knowledge of their operation is essential if full benefit is to be derived from the information they can provide. The chapter begins by looking in more detail at the sort of information provided by these satellites, then examines the satellite systems currently employed by both East and West.

WEATHER INFORMATION

Meteorological satellites can image the scene below them using a variety of sensors tuned to a number of wavelengths, both in the visible and infra-red part of the spectrum. Images taken using the visible spectrum show cloud cover and the trained meteorologist can interpret the sort of weather which these clouds carry. Using a series of such pictures, he can assess the direction and speed of the cloud movement and predict the time of arrival at any location.

Even more information can be gathered using the infra-red part of the spectrum. This part of the electromagnetic spectrum is used to deduce information about the temperature of the source of the radiation. A black and white picture is obtained, but the various shades of grey indicate the different temperatures within the region being imaged. Put simply, the whiter the area appears, the colder it is. By comparing the image with a calibrated grey scale, relative surface temperatures can be measured to an accuracy of 0.2 °C. By subsequently relating these relative temperatures to measurements taken by weather stations, the actual temperature at all points in the image can be found.

Such infra-red imagery of the sea surface can indicate sudden changes in water temperature, referred to as sea fronts. Knowledge of the existence and location of such fronts is very important to the navy and maritime aviators searching for submarines. Sonar signals propagate very differently in different water temperatures and there are often anomalous reflections from the sea front itself. The Royal Navy constantly monitors the position of such sea fronts and, cloud permitting, meterological satellites can provide timely information of their location.

Meteorological satellites typically use about five sensors operating in different bands, giving a number of images of the same scene. Each of these images will be subtly different due to the different frequencies being used to image the scene. The only satisfactory way to compare the images and fully exploit the information contained in them is to use a computer to process the data. Although the differences in the images are small, computers can accentuate them, exaggerating the temperature differences picked up by the various infra-red detectors. Colour coding techniques can then be employed, enabling various sea temperatures, and the sea fronts themselves, to be found more easily.

A technique of particular use to aviators is one known as 'atmospheric sounding', which enables vertical temperature profiles to be measured, giving more accurate information regarding pressure systems. By monitoring specific wavelengths, the radiation given off by certain molecules in the atmosphere can be measured. The amount of radiation emitted from these molecules depends upon their temperature, which in turn depends upon their height in the atmosphere. So, by measuring the radiation they emit, thereby finding their height, then comparing this height to a standard, it is possible to tell whether the molecules are lower or higher in the atmosphere than normal. This in turn gives pressure information from which wind speed and direction can be calculated.

The satellite systems used to provide weather information fall into two groups. First, there are polar-orbiting satellites, moving in low orbits inclined at approximately 98 degrees to make them Sun-synchronous. These polar-orbiting satellites image every point on the globe twice a day, once during the day and once at night. Second, there are geostationary satellites, suspended 36,000 km above the equator. These observe almost a complete hemisphere of the world continuously. A system of such satellites around the equator is used to provide worldwide cover. Both satellite groups will now be considered in more detail.

POLAR ORBITING METEOROLOGICAL SATELLITES

NOAA Satellites

NOAA stands for the National Oceanic and Atmospheric Administration in the United States. NOAA maintains two satellites in near-polar orbits at an altitude of approximately 850 km. The orbits of these satellites are separated by 90 degrees of longitude. Thus a point on the Earth's surface will pass under an orbit four times in 24 hours, thereby allowing four images to be received per day. This information from the satellites can be picked up by anyone with a suitable receiver. In fact over 120 countries subscribe to the system, and imagery is regularly used by the meteorological office in the UK.

The satellites currently used by NOAA are Advanced Tiros-N satellites. The first of this type was launched on 27 June 1979 and became known as NOAA-6. The two satellites in use today are NOAA-10, launched on 17 September 1986, and NOAA-11, launched on 24 September 1988. NOAA-10 is in the 'morning orbit' with equatorial crossings at 0730 hours local time. NOAA-11 is in the 'afternoon orbit' with equatorial crossings at 1400 hours local time. Each orbit has a period of approximately 100 minutes.

NOAA satellites monitor the weather conditions below their orbits and relay this information to Earth in two ways. First, they continuously transmit information about the picture they can see, referred to as APT (Automatic Picture Transmission). These transmissions can be received by anyone within line of sight of the satellite. Alternatively, the satellite can store the images and relay them when over Washington, where they are processed and knitted together to produce a composite image. The latter method highlights the capability of such meteorological satellites to provide information about areas remote from the home base. This information is of high quality, providing a resolution of approximately 1 km in the visible wavelengths, and temperatures accurate to within about 0.2 °C. It is important to note that this quality is available over the complete globe. Images provided by NOAA satellites are shown in Plates 7.1. and 7.2 and give a clear indication of the quality of imagery that can be obtained. In both pictures, the lighter cloud is high whereas the darker regions represent sea fog.

The primary sensors carried on board the satellites are the AVHRR (Advanced Very High Resolution Radiometer) and the TOVS (Tiros Operational Vertical Sounder). The AVHRR has five channels providing images in the visible, near infrared and far infra-red wavelengths. Data from these sensors is processed to provide information of global cloud coverage, between 20,000 and 40,000 sea surface temperature observations, and maps showing the general health of vegetation. In addition, high resolution image data is used to define sea and ice conditions, ice flow boundaries and subtle sea surface temperature differences. The TOVS complements this information by providing vertical temperature and humidity profiles through the atmosphere. It also provides information on the temperature of clouds and can even be used to measure surface temperatures under partial cloud cover.

The NOAA craft can also receive, process, and retransmit data supplied by balloons, buoys and remote stations distributed around the globe, enabling a more complete picture to be built up. The satellites also carry receivers capable of locating emergency transmitters carried by ships and aircraft, forming part of the COSPAS–

PLATE 7.1. NOAA composite of Northern Europe. (*UK National Remote Sensing Centre*)

SARSAT system. This is dealt with in more detail later in the book. The most recent satellite to be launched, NOAA-11, also carries a Solar Backscatter Ultraviolet Spectral Radiometer, which will be used to map the Earth's ozone layer by measuring the amount of UV (ultra-violet) radiation which is reflected back from the atmosphere. NOAA scientists will receive a complete ozone pattern for the entire planet every day.

NOAA is a very valuable system, used throughout the world by both military and civilian subscribers. In the UK, NOAA information is received by the RAE (Royal Aerospace Establishment) at Lasham and is passed to the Meteorological Office at Bracknell and to RAE Farnborough using METSATNET (Meteorological Satellite Network). From Farnborough the data is forwarded to military users at Northwood and Oakhanger.

The next system to be considered is dedicated to military use and its data is therefore not so widely available.

DMSP Satellites

The Defense Meteorological Satellite Programme (DMSP) is operated by the United States. Although the satellites are very similar to those used by NOAA, they are primarily for military use. Plate 7.3 shows a DMSP spacecraft. The satellites transmit their signals in a coded form so only specified US forces are able to receive their information.

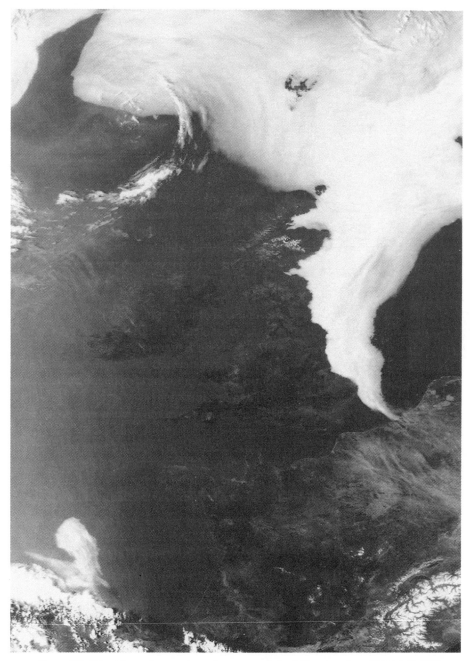

PLATE 7.2. Cloud formations and sea fog surround the UK, taken from NOAA-7. (*UK National Remote Sensing Centre*)

As in the NOAA system, two satellites are normally used in Sun-synchronous, near-polar orbits, giving equatorial crossings at 0600 and 1030 hours. The latest launch of a DMSP satellite occurred on 3 February 1988, and the satellite has an expected operational life of three years. A lower orbital height of approximately

PLATE 7.3. The DMSP satellite. (*US Space Command, 2nd Space Wing*)

500 km and a swath width of 2,960 km helps DMSP satellites to achieve a better resolution than achieved by NOAA—in fact about 500 metres using the visible spectrum.

The systems data management unit can process and record data supplied by 12 sensors, the most important of which is the Operational Linescan System, used to image a scene in both visible and infra-red wavelengths. DMSP satellites also carry sensors very similar to the TOVS equipment used by NOAA satellites. These are used to provide temperature and humidity profiles of the atmosphere. In addition, a precipitating electron spectrometer accurately locates auroral boundaries, and this information is used to aid radar and long-range ground communications in northern latitudes.

Weather information is stored on board the spacecraft before transfer to one of two 'command read-out sites' and thence to the US Air Force Global Weather Center at Offut Air Force Base, Nebraska and the US Navy Fleet Numerical Oceanography Center in Monterey, California. The US Army uses special receivers mounted on trucks to enable field commanders to receive accurate, up-to-date weather information allowing them to plan accordingly. Information is also made available to American fleets by means of receivers on board all major US warships

Meteor Satellite

Since 1969 the Soviet Union has also used polar-orbiting satellites to obtain meteorological, oceanographic and resource information. The system they use is known in the West as Meteor.

Three types of craft are used. Meteor-1 was the first to appear, first launched on 26 March 1969. At that time the craft did not have APT and images were stored on board the craft before being transmitted to one of the three receiving centres at Moscow, Novosibirsk and Kharbarovsk. Since 1971, however, Meteor-1 craft have incorporated APT. The orbit currently used by Meteor-1 craft is Sun-synchronous and has a mean altitude of 630 km.

Meteor-2 craft first appeared in 1975 and used orbits inclined at 81 degrees with mean altitudes of 900 km. The first Meteor-3 launch was in 1985 and these craft use orbits inclined at about 82 degrees, but have a higher altitude of approximately 1,200 km.

Meteor satellites are believed to be cylindrical in shape, equipped with solar arrays mounted on wings. The spacecraft are approximately five metres long and two metres in diameter. Although cylindrical in shape, the satellites use three-axis stabilisation to maintain correct orientation. Meteor-1 craft carry two TV cameras and record images covering 30,000 km in one hour, storing the information on board before transmitting the data to the ground stations. Infra-red sensors are also carried, and radiometers measure the radiation balance of the atmosphere.

Meteor-2 spacecraft are more advanced and are believed to use scanning radiometers similar to those fielded by the GOES and METEOSAT satellites described later. Several satellites are used together, in a variety of orbital planes (all inclined at approximately 81 degrees) to give weather pictures at approximately four-hourly intervals.

Few details are available regarding the Meteor-3 craft and few launches have been observed since 1985. In September 1986 Meteor-3 was found to be providing poor quality photographs. It may be that this type of craft has been discontinued.

GEOSTATIONARY METEOROLOGICAL SATELLITES

The satellites considered so far in this chapter have been polar-orbiting craft at relatively low altitude. Another group of satellites has been placed in geostationary orbit to provide a continuous watch on the weather systems of the world. Five geostationary locations are currently used and these are summarised in Figure 7.1.

Satellite	Nationality	Longitude
GOES	US	75°W
		135°W
METEOSAT	ESA	0°W
INSAT	India	74°E
GMS	Japan	140°E

Fig. 7.1. Geostationary Meteorological Satellites.

All these satellites are non-military systems, but naturally the information they provide is combined with weather information from other sources to keep military commanders fully briefed. Two systems will now be considered in some detail: METEOSAT and GOES.

METEOSAT Satellite

METEOSAT provides the ESA's contribution to the international World Weather Watch of the Global Atmospheric Research Programme. Eight European nations participate: Belgium, Denmark, France, West Germany, Italy, Sweden, Switzerland and the UK. Images provided by METEOSAT are well known to all TV viewers, although the spectacular pictures provided of the Earth's weather patterns are only a part of the programme's mission. The satellite's main task is to collect digital data from which a mathematical model of the Earth's atmosphere can be built up. Eventually, this database will enable more accurate long-term weather forecasts to be made. METEOSAT spacecraft are also used to relay weather information between ground stations around the globe.

The first METEOSAT satellite, designated F-1, was launched from Kourou in 1971. It was only partly successful as an electrical malfunction in 1973 prevented images being transmitted. In June 1981 a second satellite, designated F-2, was launched which was more successful. Although F-2's data relay facility failed, the images provided were of extremely high quality. F-2's relay problem was circumvented by using F-1 in conjunction with it to provide full facilities until 1985 when F-1 had to be de-activated when its fuel ran out. From 1985 until recently, the data relay function was carried out by a NOAA GOES satellite.

On 15 June 1988 METEOSAT P2 was launched successfully on board an Ariane-4 launcher. The satellite was actually built over 10 years ago, but was refurbished to provide a qualification model for the planned operational system of three new METEOSATS due to take up their positions in the geostationary orbit in 1989. It has relieved the GOES spacecraft of its data relay function and also provides some data of its own from a high-resolution radiometer. Meanwhile, METEOSAT F-2, whose lifetime had been extended into 1989 by carrying out a small inclination adjustment in 1986, continues to provide high quality imagery of the Earth's weather systems.

The main sensor on board the F-2 craft is a Ritchey-Chretien telescope. This telescope has an aperture of 40 cm, capable of rotating orthogonally to the spacecraft's spin axis. Data is provided in the visible (0.5 to 0.9 micrometres), thermal infra-red (10.5 to 12.5 micrometres) and water vapour absorption frequencies (5.7 to 7.1 micrometres).

Each spin of the satellite allows the thermal infra-red and water vapour absorption sensors to scan across the Earth's surface, producing a line of data. This line of data is sampled 2,500 times and these 2,500 pixels are digitally encoded and transmitted to the ground station immediately. The telescope then swivels through 26 seconds of arc and on the next rotation of the spacecraft it produces another line of data. Two and a half thousand lines are used to image the whole surface of the Earth, producing a total of 2,500 by 2,500 = 6,250,000 pixels, yielding a resolution of 5 km.

In the visible spectrum, two smaller sensors are used to produce two lines of data every spin. These lines are sampled at twice the rate of the other sensors, providing four times the amount of data in the visible part of the spectrum and yielding better resolution of 2.5 km. It takes the telescope 30 minutes to complete a whole scan, enabling two images to be transmitted every 30 minutes: one in the visible spectrum and one using the thermal infra-red or water vapour absorption frequencies.

The satellite is monitored and controlled from the European Satellite Operation Centre at Darmstadt in West Germany. Although the data is immediately available in an unprocessed form, the ground station also corrects the images for distortion and retransmits them, together with a host of information gathered from other sources, via the satellite to user stations using two relay channels. METEOSAT imagery is received in the UK at RAE Lasham and enters the METSATNET net

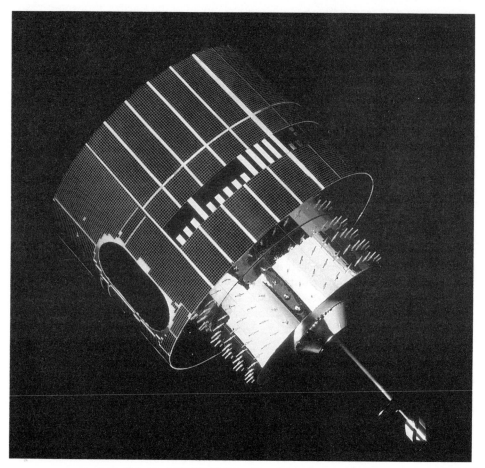

PLATE 7.4. The METEOSAT Satellite. (*Marconi Space Systems*)

together with data from the NOAA polar-orbiting satellites. Plate 7.4 shows a picture of METEOSAT. The imaging window can clearly be seen on the side of the

PLATE 7.5. The view of Earth from METEOSAT (*UK National Remote Sensing Centre*)

craft. A good example of the imagery which can be obtained is shown in Plate 7.5, giving a marvellous view of the Earth's weather system.

GOES Satellite

NOAA in the United States has always strived for a full complement of two polar-orbiting and three geostationary meteorology satellites to provide the required coverage. The polar-orbiting craft have already been described. The geostationary spacecraft are called GOES (Geostationary Operational Environmental Satellites) and these will now be examined in more detail.

The GOES series began with GOES-1, launched on 16 October 1975, by a Delta rocket from Cape Canaveral. Usually, two GOES satellites are on station at any time, at locations 75 degrees west and 135 degrees west, referred to as GOES East and GOES West. Lately, however, bad luck has struck the system and currently only one satellite, GOES-7, is operational, trying to cover both locations. GOES-7 was moved to 108 degrees west for the 1988/89 winter storm season and will move to 98 degrees west for the spring of 1989. The problem should resolve itself when the GOES Next series is launched, starting in 1990.

The most important instrument carried by the GOES craft is the VAS (Visible Infra-Red Spin-Scan Radiometer Atmospheric Sounder). Working in much the same way as the equipment on board METEOSAT, this equipment produces line-scan images of the Earth every 30 minutes. The GOES craft uses a stepping motor to move the scanner between each line. This motor is controlled by an incandescent lamp and photocell assembly to position accurately the scanning mirror before the next pass. Unfortunately, these lamps have had a tendency to burn out, limiting the lifetime of the craft to approximately three years, rather than the five years originally envisaged.

Image data generated by the VAS is received at Suitland, Maryland, processed and retransmitted via the satellite to ground stations. In this country, satisfactory reception is usually achieved by RAE Lasham, although the GOES East location is only 1.3 degrees above the horizon.

In 1985 the Ford Aerospace and Communications Corporation was awarded a contract from NOAA to provide three more satellites, known as the GOES Next series. These are due to start replacing the older GOES craft in 1990.

SUMMARY

Today's modern processing techniques allow a great deal of information to be gained from meteorological satellites. Cloud types can be observed and their heights measured. The movement of cloud structures can be measured, enabling time of arrival to be predicted and the position of weather fronts to be estimated. In addition, sea surface temperatures can be measured and the position of sea fronts can be found. Ice edges can be identified and the formation of new ice and leads in the ice pack monitored. More advanced techniques even allow fog to be identified and fog formation to be predicted. This information, when used wisely by a military commander, can be a deciding factor in determining the outcome of a conflict any-where on the globe.

8

Surveillance From Space

IMPORTANT OF SURVEILLANCE

IMPORTANCE OF SURVEILLANCE

Military surveillance is undoubtedly the most important use to which satellites have ever been put. Such a statement could be justified with numbers alone, since around 40 per cent of all satellites ever launched have been for surveillance of one form or another. However, the statement can also be justified in terms of strategic importance. After Gary Powers' U2 aircraft was shot down by the Soviets in 1960, surveillance satellites provided the only accurate means by which the west could gather information for targeting ICBMs. Later, when the various SALT (Strategic Arms Limitation) Treaties were signed, it was the surveillance satellite that provided a major means of verifying those treaties. Indeed, the term 'national technical means of verification' used in such treaties is often a euphemism for surveillance satellites. More recently, cruise missiles have been developed whose navigation systems contain detailed profiles of the terrain over selected parts of the route to their targets. Such terrain profiles can be gathered covertly from space, since a potential enemy is scarcely likely to allow teams of military surveyors access to its countryside. Coming right up to date, the warhead of the Pershing 2 missile is terminally guided to its target by a system which correlates its radar picture with a previously stored image. Again, such a stored image could be collected from space-based systems.

Surveillance from space today covers many parts of the electromagnetic spectrum: infra-red, ultra violet, radio and radar, as well as optical wavelengths. The topic covers some of the most covert of national projects both in the East and the West. Surprisingly, however, there is much open literature on these supposedly highly classified systems. The following chapter has been compiled from a variety of such open sources.

Resolution

Before proceding further, system resolution must be defined, because the main thrust in developing surveillance systems over the years has been to be to improve their resolution. This is true not only in the optical wavelengths, but also for other parts of the electromagnetic spectrum.

If the resolution of a system is defined as being, say, one metre, then it does not mean that the system can see things sized one metre or longer. Rather, it means that the system cannot distinguish between two objects which are closer together than one metre. This precise definition explains why surprisingly small objects sometimes

appear on images with quite poor resolutions. For example, power lines have sometimes been seen in favourable conditions on space imagery with a 20-metre resolution.

A moment's consideration reveals that resolution also serves as a description of
the smallest increase in size of an object which can be detected by the surveillance
system. Couple this knowledge with some political considerations and it becomes
straightforward to calculate the approximate resolution of modern space surveillance systems. Among other things, the SALT II agreement stipulated that existing
ICBMs could not have any improvements which would change their length or diameter by more than five per cent. The smallest Soviet ICBM at that time was the
SS-11, which was around two metres in diameter. Optical satellites were to be used
as the United States' means of technical verification, so the resolution had to be at
least as good as five per cent of two metres, ie around 0.1 metre (10 cm).

Clearly, the better the resolution, the more detailed the intelligence that can be
gathered. Five general levels of precision are often referred to: detection, recog-

Target	Level of Precision				
	Detection	Recognition	Identification	Description	Technical Intelligence
Bridge	6.0 m	4.5 m	1.5 m	1.0 m	30 cm
Airfield facilities	6.0 m	4.5 m	3.0 m	0.30 m	15 cm
Rockets	1.0 m	0.50 m	0.15 m	0.05 m	3 cm
Surface ships	15.0 m	4.5 m	0.15 m	0.05 m	4 cm
Submarines	7.5 m	4.0 m	0.15 m	0.05 m	2.5 cm
Aircraft	4.5 m	1.5 m	0.15 m	0.05 m	3 cm
Vehicles	1.5 m	0.50 m	0.15 m	0.05 m	3 cm

FIG 8.1. Resolutions necessary for different levels of target assessment.

nition, identification, description, and technical intelligence. Figure 8.1 gives an idea
of the approximate resolution needed for these different levels of precision, for
different targets.

Once the target and required level of precision are known, a suitable sensor
must be chosen to give that level of precision. For the very highest centimetric
resolutions one is currently limited to using optical wavelengths for the
surveillance sensor.

The angular resolution capability of any surveillance device is directly
proportional to the wavelength of the incoming signal (light or radar, etc) and
inversely proportional to the aperture diameter of the collection device (lens or

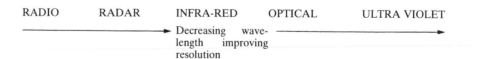

FIG 8.2. Wavelengths of surveillance sensors.

antenna) so, as Figure 8.2 shows, one can expect low (good) resolutions from optical sensors, and lens diameters or antenna widths to be made as large as possible.

OPTICAL SURVEILLANCE

Optical Surveillance Orbits

The first point to make about optical surveillance from space is to emphasise an observation made in Chapter 2 on orbital dynamics: very often the orbital parameters of a satellite give away its role. A typical optical surveillance orbit is slightly elliptical with a perigee at perhaps 150 km and an apogee around 400 km, giving an overall orbital period of around 90 minutes. The perigee is more likely to be in the northern hemisphere and on the sunlit side of the Earth. What makes such an orbit unique for optical surveillance is that it comes down low at perigee into the denser atmosphere and the increased drag will shorten the satellite's life dramatically. Clearly, there must be a good reason for doing this, and of course the reason is to allow the satellite's long focal length cameras to get the very best detail as it passes over its target at perigee. So the orbital details disclose several things. First, we have deduced it is an optical surveillance satellite. Second, we can assume that the target to be photographed will have the same latitude as the orbit perigee, so we can narrow down the areas of interest. Finally, by looking at the lighting conditions around the perigee latitude, we can narrow down the possible times of photographic activity.

There are many other less easily distinguishable orbits used by optical surveillance satellites; for example, circular orbits at 350 km altitude, with orbital planes inclined at around 70 degrees. From such orbital parameters it would be difficult to deduce the role of the craft without other intelligence. The intelligence communities have therefore studied the patterns of spacecraft operation for many years, and most low Earth orbit craft exhibit orbits or behaviour patterns which fit them into well-known categories. For instance, knowledge that the Soviet third generation surveillance satellites usually fly for 14 days before they are recovered and also fly in quite distinct bands of heights and inclinations reveals a distinct pattern of operations. Other satellites may be observed returning capsules of exposed film to Earth, and so on.

The final optical surveillance orbit worthy of mention is the Sun-synchronous orbit, described in Chapter 2. Generally speaking, a satellite in a low Earth orbit inclined at around 98 degrees will be Sun-synchronous, therefore it can be assumed that there are optical sensors on board. Sun-synchronous satellites are long-lifetime craft by design and therefore have to fly higher than the low perigee type. Such orbits are used by some civil remote-sensing craft, some meteorological satellites and, reportedly, by the latest generation of American military optical surveillance satellites. Such long orbital lifetimes suggest that all such craft use electro-optical sensors, rather than film, to record their observations, and data is transmitted back to Earth by radio link.

The fact that all these orbits have something like a 90-minute orbital period does not, however, mean that such a satellite could photograph a static location every 90 minutes. Remember that the orbital plane of a satellite remains fixed in direction in space while the Earth rotates beneath the orbit. So for any single satellite, a particular location will pass under the orbital plane twice a day: once per day on the light side of the Earth and once per day on the dark side. Each satellite therefore has only one daytime photographic opportunity per day. Admittedly, the satellite could try an oblique shot on adjacent passes, but for the highest resolution the overhead or near overhead photograph gives the best results. So, in practical terms, each satellite has only one high resolution photographic opportunity per day on any one target.

One photograph per day may be acceptable, but optical photography and, to a lesser extent, infra-red are thwarted by cloud cover. Such restrictions cause no problem for photographing desert scenes, but over Europe the skies may be clear enough for satellite photography for only about 20 per cent of the time. It is therefore difficult to guarantee photography from space. This lack of guaranteed availability is one of the factors which dictate that photography from space is not really the sort of information that can be used tactically. Such intelligence lends itself more to being pieced together over time, so is better thought of as a strategic planning aid.

Another consideration which reinforces the non-tactical nature of photographs is the time taken to make use of the information gathered. If photographic film is used, it must be brought back to Earth, collected, processed and scrutinised. Intelligence reports then have to be written, disseminated and digested. Days may elapse between the photograph being taken and consequent action. Although photographic film is still used in some surveillance satellites, the trend is now towards more real-time capabilities for data collection. Film is, however, capable of giving very high resolutions, so we may expect to see such satellites in operation for some time to come.

Civil Programmes

Before turning our attention to specific military programmes, it is worth spending some time considering current civil or commercial surveillance satellite programmes, usually referred to as 'remote-sensing' programmes. These programmes are becoming increasingly important and, as the resolutions improve, so the military powers of many nations are becoming even more interested in the commercial products available.

For surveillance data to be useful for military purposes, one would generally need a resolution of around 25 metres or better. Clearly, the higher the resolution the better, but at around 25 metres large buildings, road structures, rivers, lakes, etc, become distinguishable. The US Landsat series of satellites provide such resolution and have for many years been the work-horses of many civil remote-sensing programmes. Data from the seven frequency bands of Landsat's thematic mapper can be processed in a variety of ways to highlight healthy vegetation, pollution, etc, and have provided a wealth of economic intelligence.

In 1986 the French launched the first of their planned series of SPOT (Système pour l'Obervation de la Terre) satellites, which give a resolution of 20 metres for multispectral images and 10 metres for black and white. For many years 10 metres was a significant limiting resolution on civil systems because the United States refused to launch commercial satellites whose resolution was better than 10 metres. However, in early 1987, the Soviet Union's Soyuzkarta agency surprised the world

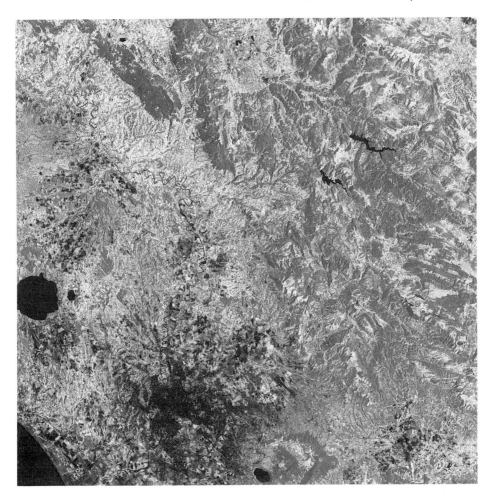

PLATE 8.1. A Landsat-5 thematic mapper image of the area around Rome, Italy. (*Image: produced by Space Department, RAE Farnborough*)

by offering nations five-metre resolution photography of their own countries. Also, the non-US commercial launch agencies had no limiting policies on resolution. The United States recognised not only that the 'clear skies' monopoly enjoyed by the Superpowers was coming to an end, but also that there was a danger that good commercial launch contracts would be lost. Therefore, bowing to commercial pressure, the United States announced in early 1987 that its 10-metre launch limit had been lifted. World news agencies are already considering the cost-effectiveness of high resolution, five metres or so, surveillance from space.

At present Soyuzkarta products offer the highest commercially available resolutions, quoted at five metres average resolution, but in fact imagery assessed at 1.3 metres resolution in the high contrast areas has been reportedly received by customers.

In summary, the gap is slowly closing between military and civil optical surveillance resolutions, but there is some way to go before photographs of a few centi-metres of resolution become freely available to the public at large.

UNITED STATES' OPTICAL SURVEILLANCE PROGRAMME

The United States' space-based optical surveillance programme is shrouded in secrecy but that shroud has worn fairly thin in places, allowing some visibility. It is widely reported in the open press that the programme is overseen by the US National Reconnaissance Office and that the surveillance satellites are referred to as the Keyhole Satellite Program. The United States officially still refuses to publish details of the programme despite it having been discussed openly on the floor of the House of Representatives and despite the fact that the Soviets clandestinely purchased an operator's manual for one of the latest generation KH-11 satellites for $3,000 in 1977!

Keyhole Satellite Program

The roots of the Keyhole Satellite Program go back to the late 1950s, starting with the Discoverer programme which was mainly for research and development but was also reportedly a cover for an early CIA (Central Intelligence Agency) surveillance satellite programme called CORONA. Between February 1959 and February 1962, 38 Discoverer satellite launches were made. Early launches were mainly experi-mental and there were many failures, but by mid-1961 fairly good photographic results were being achieved.

In October 1960 the US Air Force launched SAMOS 1 which was the first US attempt to launch a fully operational photo reconnaissance satellite. The launch failed but SAMOS 2 did work successfully in January 1961, reportedly providing intelligence with around six metres resolution. Later SAMOS satellites may have had resolutions of around two to three metres. Being the first operational system, SAMOS is also referred to as Keyhole 1 (KH-1). Since SAMOS 2's launch in January 1961, the United States has successfully orbited over 200 photo reconnaissance satellites in systems of increasing complexity. The consensus opinion of the space press is currently that KH-11 is the latest of the series to be orbited and even more advanced craft are about to be launched.

Concentrating on the more recent developments, Figure 8.3 shows the Keyhole satellite on-orbit programme for the 1980s, during which time three main satellite types were reportedly used KH-8, KH-9 (Big Bird) and KH-11.

KH-8 Satellite

First launched in July 1966, 51 KH-8 series satellites were launched in a 100 per cent successful series ending in August 1984. A typical KH-8 orbit was Sun-synchronous with an apogee of around 475 km and a perigee of around 155 km. It is reported that at perigee the KH-8 would be capable of around 15 cm resolution. KH-8 is significant in that it was the last of its kind. Exposed film was loaded into canisters which were de-orbited in the area around Hawaii. Specially equipped aircraft would snatch the canisters from the sky as they descended on their para-

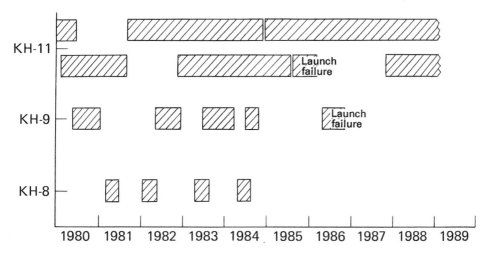

FIG 8.3. The US optical surveillance satellite programme for the 1980s.

chutes. The film then had to be flown back to base, developed and despatched to the assessing agency. Clearly, the chain of events from the photograph being taken to the final intelligence assessment took quite a long time, so later series of US satellites have used techniques to speed up the return of the data, albeit at the expense of resolution in some cases.

KH-9 (Big Bird) Satellite

First launched in June 1971, Big Bird represented a major improvement over KH-8. First, the satellite weighed nearly five times as much as KH-8 and was 15 metres long by 3 metres in diameter (hence the name!). In addition to both wide-angle and high-resolution cameras, Big Bird was also reported to have infra-red and multispectral scanners. About six returnable film canisters were used, again recovered by the same airborne snatch system as employed by KH-8. However, in addition to this standard recovery method, there was also a capability for scanned images to be transmitted to Earth via a radio data link when a direct line of sight existed between the satellite and a ground station. The resolution would suffer using this technique but the retrieval of the data was much faster. The Big Bird, destroyed on launch in 1986, was reported to be the last in the US inventory.

KH-11 Satellite

KH-11 represents the latest generation of optical space reconnaissance craft. The satellite carries no film, but instead uses electro-optical devices which scan the area of interest in several spectral bands and transmit the data back to Earth. Although early KH-11 pictures were reportedly not as good as film photographs, the gap between the resolutions appears to have closed. Open press articles speculate a resolution of around 5–10 cm for the latest KH-11s.

Public knowledge of the capability to produce such very high resolution optical images from space was mere informed speculation until, in August 1984, Samuel Loring Morison, who worked at the US Naval Intelligence Support Center, took three classified KH-11 photographs and gave them to *Jane's Defence Weekly* magazine. The pictures were published and Mr Loring was subsequently jailed for two years for theft and espionage.

KH-11 is another large craft, around 19 metres long and weighing about the same as Big Bird. The first craft was launched in December 1976, since when eight have been launched. Again, the craft uses a Sun-synchronous polar orbit. Because a direct line-of-sight radio link does not always exist between KH-11 and its control centres, the craft is reported to have the capability to relay its data through data relay satellites, such as the US geostationary TDRS system. KH-11 has an extremely long lifetime in comparison to both KH-8 and -9; 700 days is not unusual. To exploit such a long lifetime, the orbits are necessarily higher, with apogee around 600 km and perigee around 325 km.

Trends in the US Programme

Throughout the 1980s there has been a continuous improvement in the capabilities of US optical reconnaissance satellites. Resolutions have been driven down by, among other things, the verification requirements of the SALT II agreement. The main change from KH-8 to KH-11 has been the speed of recovery of the data, from days with the capsule system of KH-8, to minutes using the near real-time data link from KH-11, perhaps via a relay comsat. The lack of dependence on film has led to the possibility of much longer operational durations. KH-11's operational life is

Satellite	Main Parameters (approx)					
	Weight (kg)	Mean apogee (km)	Mean perigree (km)	Mean life (days)	Data return	Data retrieval time
KH-8	3,000	475	155	28	2 capsules	Days
KH-9	13,300	317	195	130	6 capsules + data link	Hours
KH-11	13,300	600	325	~700	Near real-time link via relay satellite	Minutes

FIG 8.4. Main parameters of the US optical surveillance satellites used during the 1980s.

probably limited only by manoeuvring propellant reserves. Figure 8.4 summarises the main parameters of the US Keyhole satellites flown during the 1980s.

SOVIET UNION'S OPTICAL SPACE SURVEILLANCE PROGRAMME

The Soviet Union's optical space surveillance programme no doubt achieves similar results to the United States' but, interestingly, the Soviets go about business in a significantly different way. The United States launched 16 optical surveillance satellites during the period 1980–89; in contrast, the Soviets are reported to have launched around 320 over the same period. However, like the United States, the

Soviets are now moving towards a more real-time capability. A launch pattern has emerged over the years and the Western press has taken delight in making the pattern public. So let us apply that pattern to Farnborough's openly published 1987 satellite tables and examine the programme in some detail (see Figure 8.5).

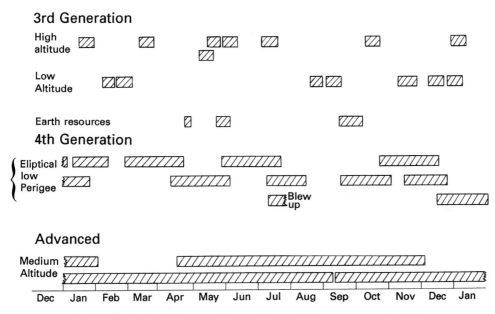

FIG 8.5. The Soviet Union's optical surveillance satellite programme for 1987.

Third Generation Reconnaissance Satellites

The first class of craft to consider is often referred to as the third generation craft, which is reportedly based on the Vostok vehicle which took Yuri Gagarin into orbit. Typically, the craft has a 14-day mission, after which the craft recovers to Earth for film retrieval and analysis. A pattern of three distinctly different modes of operation has emerged for this type of craft.

First, the craft is flown at around 355–415 km altitude in its medium resolution role in 70–73 degree inclined orbits. Using similar inclinations, the craft is also used at much lower altitudes with perigees of 170–200 km. If the systems on board both types are identical, halving the height would double the resolution. The final role of the craft is for Earth Resources observation. Heights in this role are typically around 250 km but use a unique inclination band of 82–83 degrees. The number of craft used in the Earth Resources role has been steadily decreasing for some years as Landsat type remote-sensing satellites may be superceding this older film-carrying class of craft.

Fourth Generation Reconnaissance Satellites

First flown in 1975, the Soviet's fourth generation reconnaissance satellites may well be based on Soyuz hardware. They fly for significantly longer missions than the third generation and reportedly return film canisters to Earth during the mission to extend the time on orbit. Early missions were around 30 days in length but have been gradually lengthening; the 1987 average was 48 days and the maximum seen is 59 days. The craft are easily distinguished by their 64.8–67.1-degree inclined eliptical orbits with low 170–200-km perigees, combined with the 30–59-day lifetimes. These craft are reported to produce the highest resolution photographs for the Soviets.

Advanced Systems

The first Soviet advanced photo reconnaissance satellite was launched in 1982, since when mission lengths have grown from 67 days to the current record of 259 days. From Figure 8.5, it would appear that the operational goal may well be coverage by two of these satellites at all times. The long orbital lifetimes and the lack of reports of any film capsules returning to Earth suggest that this craft is similar in role to the American KH-11 electro-optical satellite. If the shape and weight figures in Farnborough's satellite tables are to be believed, the Soviet advanced systems are somewhat similar to the fourth generation satellites in external appearance and weight but are only around half the size of an American KH-11.

Trends in the Soviet Programme

Although the Soviets have acquired a near real-time capability for recovering imagery from space with their advanced satellites, they have not let up in the rate of launch of their film-carrying satellites, with the exception of the Earth Resources vehicles. The photo surveillance task continues to account for around one-third of all Soviet launches.

The main difference between the US and Soviet programmes would appear to be flexibility. On 1 June 1987, for instance, the United States had one KH-11 on orbit whereas the Soviets had no fewer than six photo surveillance vehicles in use. In times of tension, therefore, the Soviets may be in a better position to monitor a developing situation closely by launching one or more craft whose orbits are specifically tailored to cover a particular location.

INFRA-RED SURVEILLANCE FROM SPACE

Both cloud and darkness limit the use of Earth photography at optical wavelengths. However, by looking in the near infra-red wavelengths, Earth surveillance may still be possible in the dark and through light cloud. Unfortunately, resolution becomes worse at the longer infra-red wavelengths and will not give the centrimetric clarity of optical wavelengths. Nevertheless, infra-red systems will be used for many years to come to extend the limits of coverage for surveillance satellites.

Infra-red systems really come into their own when used to detect and classify hot objects against a cold background and there are systems both on orbit and under development which perform in just this way.

ICBM Launch Warning from Space

Both the United States and the Soviet Union use infra-red satellites as part of their early warning network to detect the launch of ICBMs.

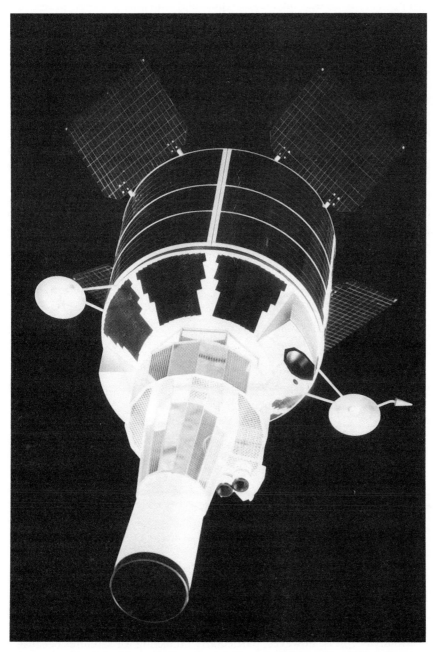

PLATE 8.2. The United States Defense Support Program (DSP) satellite. (*USAF Photo*)

The American system is known as the DSP (Defense Support Program) and consists of several satellites, spaced around the equator in geostationary orbits. Each satellite (see Plate 8.2) consists of a large and powerful infra-red telescope designed to detect the launch of ICBMs from the Earth's surface, or when they break through cloud cover. The satellite will calculate launch positions and, by analysis of the hot exhaust plume, will classify the missile types. DSP will not, however, predict impact points. That task is left to the BMEWS (Ballistic Missile Early Warning System) radar network on Earth. The main importance of DSP, therefore, is that it increases the warning period for an attack.

The SDI project fully recognises the importance of the role of early detection of ICBM boosters and the BSTS (Boost Surveillance Tracking System) satellite is one of the major parts of the SDI programme. BSTS will represent an extension of the capabilities of the existing DSP system.

The Soviet Union also has an ICBM launch detection constellation but again it goes about its business in a different way. Nine Soviet early warning satellites orbit the Earth in highly inclined Molniya orbits with perigee around 600 km and apogee around 40,000 km. Each 12-hour orbit is longitudinally spaced 40 degrees from the next, so that each satellite takes exactly the same ground track at 2 hour 40 minute intervals. This technique ensures that one satellite is always close to apogee and is

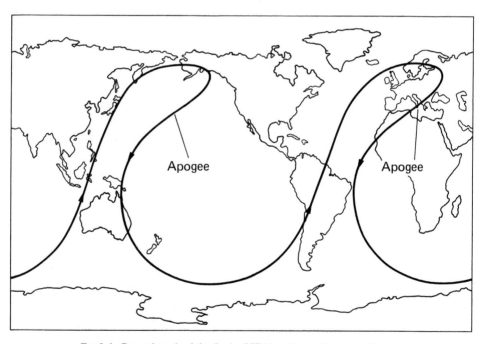

Fig 8.6. Ground track of the Soviet ICBM early warning constellation.

in a position to observe the US ICBM fields. Figure 8.6 shows the ground track of the satellites.

The Molniya orbit is, however, particularly punishing for satellites because they have to cross the Van Allen radiation belts four times a day. The Soviets have taken some time to build up the constellation and they currently have to launch around three satellites per year to keep the system fully topped up and operational.

ELECTRONIC SURVEILLANCE

Electronic surveillance from space is, in principle, the simplest of spaceborne tasks. All that is needed is a sensitive radio receiver and a tape recorder. The system can be programmed as it flies over friendly territory, then it will switch on and record over the target area. When back over friendly territory, the recorded data can be down-linked for analysis. Because there are no national boundaries in space, such devices can eavesdrop without any possible political embarrassment. Despite their importance, however, these space-based eavesdropping systems have to be viewed as an integral part of a much larger intelligence collection system using fixed and mobile sites as well as the space-based receivers.

Reportedly, the Soviet Union has had ELINT (Electronic Intelligence) satellites in space since 1967 and its current constellation consists of six satellites at 650 km altitude. Their task is to help build up a picture of the electronic order of battle of any nation of interest. The system is reputed to be able to locate the position of ground-based pulsed radars with an accuracy of around 10 km.

The United States has similar satellites on orbit. Electronic surveillance has always attracted the very highest security shielding so little, other that speculation, is reported in open literature. One sees many references to a SIGINT (Signals Intelligence) satellite code-named Rhyolite, and in a spectacular espionage trial in 1977, the American Christopher Boyce was jailed for passing Rhyolite data to the Soviets. Rhyolite-type satellites are reportedly at geostationary altitude and at that great distance will need extremely large receiving dishes to pick up the weak signals. Rhyolite's replacement is said to be a satellite code-named Aquacade, about which little has appeared in the open press, but may in fact be Rhyolite, renamed after the 1977 compromise. 1978 reportedly saw the first of the next generation of US SIGINT satellite code-named Chalet. After an article about Chalet appeared in the *New York Times*, the satellite may have been renamed Vortex. Another SIGINT satellite code-named Magnum was Shuttle-launched in January 1985 amid great secrecy, only to be fully reported later in the *Washington Post*. Such name-changing and great secrecy are typical of the security efforts of the SIGINT world.

Nuclear Burst Detection Systems

Between 1958 and 1963 the USA, UK and USSR had a series of discussions which led to the Limited Test Ban Treaty. The treaty forbade any signatory from testing nuclear weapons in either the atmosphere or in space. In October 1963 the United States launched a pair of Vela satellites whose job it was to police the treaty for the West, and look for above-ground nuclear explosions. The satellites were at 115,000 km altitude and from such extreme height they had an excellent view of the whole globe.

A nuclear explosion produces massive amounts of X-rays, Gamma rays and Neutrons, in addition to a very bright flash. The radiation also causes an intense electromagnetic pulse from atmospheric bursts. The radiation signature is complex but well understood, so Vela-type satellites are able to estimate weapon yields and, if the radiation is received by several satellites, the location of the burst can be accurately determined.

The Vela NUDET (Nuclear Detection) constellation was continuously improved and supplemented until 1970. The satellites worked very well, and some were still providing test and verification information 14 years after launch.

In the 1970s, the US NUDET role is reported to have been taken over by the ICBM launch detection satellites. For the future the task will be carried out by the NUDET payloads riding piggy-back on the Navstar GPS navigation satellites.

Apart from the test ban monitoring, a global military power such as the United States would benefit from such a capability if nuclear hostilities were ever to break out. In such times of confused communications the NUDET system may be the only reliable way of keeping track of a nuclear exchange.

RADAR SURVEILLANCE

The resolution of optical systems from space is nowadays of the order of a few centimetres and is about as good as it is going to get without a major breakthrough in optical processing. Unfortunately, optical surveillance is defeated by cloud and darkness, so cannot be guaranteed 24 hours a day. Moving to infra-red frequencies will extend the coverage factor but heavy cloud will still defeat such a system. These problems can be solved, at a stroke, by moving into the radar frequencies where true 24-hour, all-weather coverage is possible. Of course it is not quite as straightforward as that; there are at least two major concerns with space-based radars. The first problem is that of resolution. Currently, the best resolution that can be obtained using radar from space is in the tens of metres, ie, around 100 times worse that at optical frequencies. Second, it is very difficult to generate enough power to drive a conventional radar using solar panels, so a space-based radar system requires either a novel type of radar or a nuclear reactor for a power source. Both approaches are currently used.

Synthetic Aperture Radar

Just suppose that there was a requirement for a satellite surveillance system at 250 km orbital height which had to provide one-metre resolution imagery. At optical wavelengths (around 0.5 micron) this could be easily achieved with a lens of 12-cm diameter. At the longer thermal infra-red wavelengths (10 microns) a lens of 2.5 metres would be needed for the same resolution. However, at the comparatively very long centimetric radar wavelengths, that resolution would require an antenna 7.5 km long. Clearly, physically building such a structure on orbit is impractical but there is a way of fooling a radar set into thinking its antenna is very long: this technique is known as SAR (Synthetic Aperture Radar), where an extremely long antenna is sythesised by virtue of the movement of the satellite through the sky. Over a period of time the received radar returns are electronically combined and the result is as if a massive antenna had been used. Currently, 25 metres of resolution is possible from such a system in low Earth orbit, and early good results have prompted a flurry of SAR satellite projects for many military and civil uses.

The SAR technique was well illustrated in the late 1970s when the Americans flew Seasat which contained an SAR. Seasat operated for only 100 days but returned data which not only proved the technique, but also highlighted some unexpected results in the imagery.

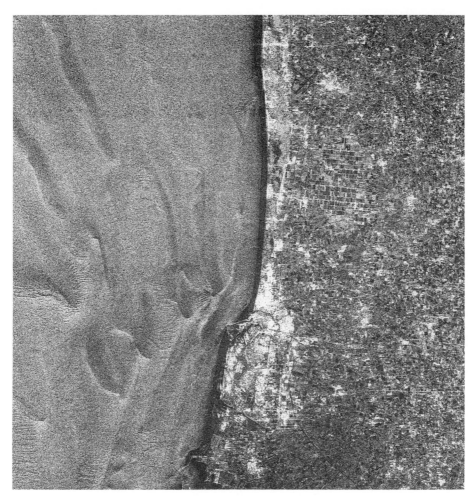

PLATE 8.3. SAR image of the Dunkerque area. (*Image: produced by Space Department, RAE, Farnborough*)

Take, for example, the image at Plate 8.3, which shows the town of Dunkirque in France and the area of the English Channel adjacent to the coast. At the time of the image, the wind and tide directions were parallel to the coast and caused the strange relief features clearly visible on the water. These features exactly match the ocean bed in that area. On the following satellite pass, the wind and tide were no longer parallel to the coast and the sea surface was uniformly flat and grey.

Another surprising aspect of SAR imagery is illustrated at Plate 8.4, which shows a bulk carrier vessel at sea, along with the ship's wake. The image of the vessel is offset from the wake because the SAR processing assumes the ship to be stationary,

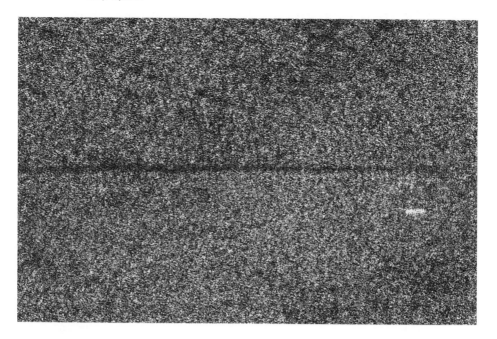

PLATE 8.4. SAR image of a ship and its wake. (*Image: produced by Space Department, RAE Farnborough*)

so the Doppler-shifted radar returns of the moving ship result in the wrong position being calculated for the vessel. However, the distance between the image of the ship and its wake is proportional to the speed of the vessel. Being able to measure a vessel's speed from space is clearly an advantage for a radar surveillance system.

A more detailed analysis of the vessel's image gives the overall shape of the superstructure. The radar returns can be density sliced and displayed to give an impression of the three-dimensional outline of the ship, as in Plate 8.5. Military vessels can have very distinctive outlines, so this technique may be useful in distinguishing between commercial and military vessels.

Several military and civil SAR programmes are planned for the future. For example, there has been speculation that SAR techniques may one day allow the detection of submerged submarines by detecting minute changes in the sea surface as the submarine passes. No doubt the improvement of resolution and processing techniques will be high priorities in such research programmes.

REAL-TIME SURVEILLANCE

Broadly speaking, intelligence data falls into two categories. First there is the type of information which ages very slowly; into this category falls the location of large fixed installations such as airfields. This 'strategic' intelligence can be collected piecemeal over long periods of time and can be updated as changes take place. At the other end of the scale there is information which ages very rapidly and must be transported for assessment as quickly as possible, perhaps so that it can be used in

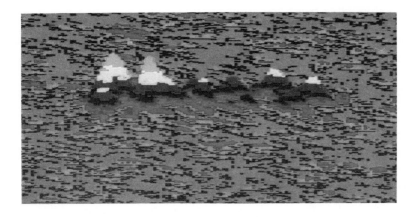

PLATE 8.5. SAR image of a bulk carrier ship. (*Image: produced by Space Department, RAE, Farnborough*)

real or near real time to assist in the management of a particular operation. The current disposition of troops or fighting units is a good example of this kind of 'tactical' intelligence.

This chapter has shown how the trend is towards the quicker return of data from space, sometimes at the expense of resolution. The problems of cloud, darkness and satellite absence at crucial times dictate that although optical surveillance is now able to return data quickly, it is unlikely to be used as the prime battle field management aid, but rather to confirm force dispositions when possible. Electronic and radar surveillance systems, on the other hand, work in all weathers, day and night. Admittedly, there is still the problem of having enough satellites to cover the targets, but in general it would appear that such systems could be used to track major, slow moving units in real time, if only for short periods. Naval vessels or groups of vessels would be ideal targets for such systems, where a resolution of several tens of metres would be acceptable. Not surprisingly, the Soviets and the Americans have such military ocean surveillance systems.

The war at sea may well be crucial in any conflict between the Superpowers. In the long term, therefore, there is a need for each side to gather detailed intelligence, but if hostilities were to break out, real-time knowledge of force strengths and dispositions would be of immense value, particularly for over-the-horizon targeting of anti-ship missiles.

Soviet Ocean Surveillance

The Soviet Union uses two space systems for real-time ocean surveillance. The EORSAT (ELINT Ocean Reconnaissance Satellite) is a passive system, like the global ELINT satellites, but EORSAT's task is to determine ships' positions by intercepting their radar transmissions. EORSAT's position-fixing capability is reported to be as accurate as 2 km. Flying at around 435 km, the satellite will have a good listening range and also a good range for transmission of intelligence to a cooperating Soviet vessel. Clearly, a complete defence against EORSAT is to go silent and switch off all transmitters, but of course a vessel would then be open to air attack. Not only that, but the vessel would still be detectable by the Soviets' active real-time surveillance system, the RORSAT (Radar Ocean Reconnaissance Satellite). Flying low, at around 255 km, RORSAT operates in conjunction with EORSAT to obtain precise positioning and dispositions of Western surface forces, and to relay that information in real time to suitably equipped vessels. It is reported that RORSAT can probably detect destroyer-sized vessels in low sea states and aircraft carrier-sized vessels in rough weather.

EORSAT/RORSAT activities are coordinated for best effect and a frequently used constellation has one of each type with their orbits spaced at 145 degrees. Both satellites use 65-degree inclined orbits. Activities frequently coincide with major Western maritime exercises and the British–Argentine conflict in the Falkland Islands was also well covered by these systems. Reports suggest that EORSATs have an operational life of something like 10 months, whereas the RORSAT has only around two to three months of life.

Providing the high power for a radar in space is a major problem which the Soviets have solved by using a nuclear reactor on board the satellite. At the end of RORSAT's operational life the reactor is split from the transmitter and boosted to around 1,000 km height, where it will have around 1,000 thousand years for the radioactive materials to decay before the reactor recovers into the Earth's atmosphere. This boosting of the reactor to high orbit is not always successful and two have recovered inadvertently to Earth. The most famous was the event on 24 January 1978 when Cosmos 954 crashed into Canada's Northwest Territories, spreading the radioactive contents of the reactor around the Canadian countryside. Another RORSAT, Cosmos 1900, also malfunctioned and in September 1988 would have re-entered intact, but a fail-safe system split the reactor away from the remainder of the satellite in the final few days of its life, and the reactor was boosted to a higher level.

US Ocean Surveillance

The United States is reported to have a capability similar to the EORSAT ocean ELINT system. The American system, White Cloud, was first launched in April 1976 and is said to consist of a mother satellite which ejects a group of three sub-satellites which fly in orbital close proximity at around 850 km altitude. The system probably uses interferometery techniques to fix the positions of naval vessels by comparing the arrival times of intercepted radar pulses from the ships at each of the sub-satellites. White Cloud is also speculated to have infra-red equipment on board to detect ships' wakes.

The US RORSAT equivalent was possibly to have been a satellite code-named Clipper Bow, but the project is reported to have been cancelled due to technical difficulty.

Relay Satellites

Throughout this chapter a trend has emerged, showing a movement towards the real or near real-time collection of data from space, not only for optical intelligence but from all parts of the electromagnetic spectrum. The main problem is that a direct line-of-sight path must exist for the data to be transmitted from a satellite to a ground control station. The advent of the relay satellite means that the satellite collecting the data will no longer have to wait for the control station to come into view. Instead, it will pass the intelligence immediately via a, perhaps geostationery, relay satellite. Both the Americans and the Soviets have such systems. A fully operational relay constellation is also considered vital to the success of the US Space Station project. The ESA is also planning to launch its own non-military relay satellite network.

9

Satellite-Aided Search and Rescue

It is bad enough to be in distress in one of the Earth's more desolate areas, but having taken the trouble to carry a distress radio beacon it must be all the more worrying if you are not sure if anyone is actually listening to your transmissions. Until relatively recent times, in truly remote areas, it could quite literally have been a matter of luck whether such transmissions were ever heard, and locating the survivor was then a race against time before the beacon's batteries wore out. However, in the mid-1970s an idea was conceived which has now come to fruition in the COSPAS/SARSAT system. The system is a truly remarkable international effort whose aim is to use the high vantage point of space to give a more reliable coverage for emergency beacons on a global basis. This chapter deals with a system which is not military by design, but is available for use by Service and civilian alike. However, parts of the overall system are operated by military personnel and SAR (Search and Rescue) is often the responsibility of military agencies.

The idea of calculating the position of earthbound transmitters, from the signals received by satellite, is not a new one, and the calculations are fairly straightforward. Indeed, it is exactly the task performed by the military ELINT satellites, and as long ago as 1969 the technique was also used with Nimbus-3 to track the migration of Canadian elks.

As a result of some early feasibility studies into the prospect of monitoring and fixing the position of emergency locator beacons from Earth-orbiting satellites, the United States, Canada and France joined forces in 1977 in the SARSAT (Search and Rescue Satellite Aided Tracking) programme. As SARSAT moved into the test phase, the Soviet Union was involved in a similar project known as COSPAS (the Russian language abbreviation of Space System for Search for Distressed Vessels). Because of the many advantages, the programmes came to an agreement in late 1979 to ensure mutual system compatibility, whilst at the same time retaining their separate identities and their completeness as individual projects.

The SAR payloads ride piggy-back on board American weather satellites and Soviet navigation satellites. The first COSPAS launch was in 1982 and SARSAT in 1983. By July 1985, when the system was declared operational, the project membership had grown to include the United States, Soviet Union, France, Canada, the UK, Norway, Sweden, Finland and Bulgaria. Since then other countries have joined the programme and several others have shown interest in joining. By any standard the system has been a success. The total number of persons rescued passed 1,000 in November 1987 and stood at 1,149 by September 1988, the system's sixth anniversary, maintaining an average rate of one person rescued every two days.

SYSTEM CONCEPT

The basic concept of the system is that payloads on two US and two Soviet near polar-orbiting satellites listen for distress transmissions on three radio frequencies.

COSPAS/SARSAT	SATELLITE	STATUS
SARSAT 2	NOAA 9	OK
SARSAT 3	NOAA 10	406-MHz processor failed/repeater OK
SARSAT 4	NOAA 11	OK
COSPAS 2	Cosmos 1447	OK
COSPAS 3	Cosmos 1574	OK

FIG 9.1. COSPAS/SARSAT constellation status as at November 1988.

The satellites currently providing the service are given at Figure 9.1. The Americans listen on 121.5, 243 and 406 MHz, but the Soviets listen only on 121.5 and 406 MHz. The location of the beacon can be calculated by monitoring the observed frequency shift of the emergency transmission as the satellite passes overhead the beacon. The range at which a beacon can be detected is a function of beacon power. Also, the accuracy with which the position of the transmitter can be fixed is highly dependent on the stability of the carrier frequency transmitted by the beacon. Unfortunately, the many 121.5- and 243-MHz emergency beacons on the market today were never designed with COSPAS/SARSAT in mind, so the carrier frequencies are a little unstable, the beacon power is often relatively low (typically 75 milliwatts) and the modulation format is not ideal for satellite tracking. Despite these minor drawbacks, COSPAS/SARSAT is able to achieve a locating accuracy of 20 km in 68 per cent of cases and within 30 km on 80 per cent of occasions at these frequencies. The frequency of 406 MHz, however, was chosen specially for SARSAT so the beacon specifications call for a much more stable frequency and a higher power output. Consequently, survivors transmitting at 406 MHz can be fixed within better than 5 km on 95 per cent of occasions.

COVERAGE

121.5- and 243-MHz distress signals require quite complicated processing to yield an acceptable fix accuracy, so the processing task is done on the ground and the satellite acts merely as a relay station for the signals at these frequencies. The signals are relayed to one of the many LUTs (Local User Terminals) scattered around the world. Clearly, in order for the satellite to relay the signals, it must be in sight of both the survivor and the LUT. The 850–1,000-km altitude of the satellites therefore restrict the areas of coverage and the system does not give global coverage at these frequencies. Typically, this means that coverage is restricted to within approximately

4,000 km of the LUTs. The survivor's position is calculated at the LUT, then passed to the nearest COSPAS/SARSAT MCC (Mission Coordination Centre). The MCC then informs the local RCC (Rescue Coordination Centre) and the SAR forces are sent into action to effect the rescue. The chain of events at 406 MHz has the same effect but is slightly different in operation. The specially designed 406-MHz beacons transmit at a recommended power of 5W, which is around 70 times the power of the lower frequency beacons. This greater power requirement is offset by the fact that the beacons only transmit for 0.44 second every 50 seconds and the digital modulation carries information on the type of user, country of origin, individual user identification, urgency code and elapsed time since the accident. Also, the message can carry 32 extra bits describing the nature of the emergency, including perhaps the location of the incident.

The clean, stable and high-powered signal structure at 406 MHz allows small but powerful processing packages to be carried in the satellites. The precise Doppler shift is calculated on board and the data, along with time and beacon identification data, are stored until an LUT comes into view, at which time the satellite downloads the data. Therefore, in contrast to the other frequencies, coverage at 406 MHz is global. Also, the system can cope with up to 90 beacons transmitting simultaneously.

Canada, France and the United States have examined the possibility of placing a SARSAT payload on a geostationary satellite. Such a satellite appears stationary in the sky, so Doppler position fixing is not possible but such a receiver would give a much quicker warning of an emergency since it can see about one-third of the Earth continuously. Also in the longer message format it is possible to include position data, so locating the incident would not be a problem. Tests have shown that the signal can be received at geostationary height and by the early 1990s, the United States, Japan and India have stated that they intend to include COSPAS payloads on their geostationary satellites.

False alarms account for around 97 per cent of the alerts on 121.5/243 MHz. The events are usually traced to careless handling of the transmitter, but at least one such incident has resulted in the recovery of a stolen beacon. Many 121.5/243-MHz false alarms are triggered by misuse of the frequencies by non-distress traffic. This is one cause which will reduce dramatically when 406 MHz becomes the predominantly used frequency, because that frequency is clear of the normal UHF voice bands. Also, because of the unique SAR format at 406 MHz, distress messages will be more readily identifiable.

As the benefits of 406 MHz become advertised more widely, so operations at that frequency are increasing. 406 MHz has been operational since 1985 and the number rescued on that frequency is growing. July 1987 saw the first sale of a British-made 406-MHz beacon and also the first British transmission at 406 MHz, when Richard Branson's record-breaking transatlantic balloon flight ended in a ditching in the Irish Sea. The sale of 406-MHz beacons passed the 2,000 mark in late 1988 and continues to rise.

Coverage of the system is growing steadily as new nations join the COSPAS/SARSAT fraternity. Brazil is the most recent nation to join, providing the first southern hemisphere LUT in 1988. India and Australia will have LUTs in 1989, Venezuela in 1990, Japan in 1992. Cyprus, Pakistan, Greece, New Zealand and Portugal are also making investigations into providing services. As more nations join, so the time to alert the rescue forces will reduce even further. In 1987 the Inmarsat organisation in London took over the task of providing an international secretariat for COSPAS/-SARSAT to cover the administrative and organisational functions and thus make the overall system more of an identifiable organisation. Also, the renewal of the COSPAS/SARSAT agreement, in 1988, for a further 15 years, has assured the existence of this superb system for the future.

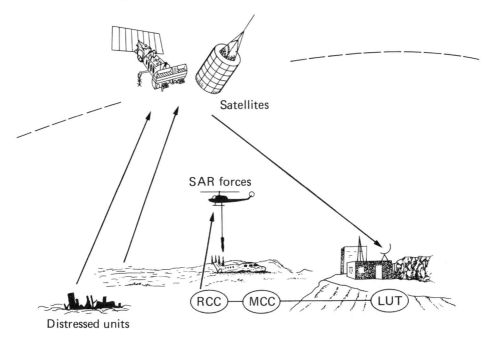

FIG 9.2. Basic concept of COSPAS/SARSAT.

Man in Space

Man in Space

Military and civil space operations have, for the most part, been conducted by unmanned satellites. Man has visited space, at times for long periods, but the extreme inhospitality of the space environment may well dictate that man can only be a visitor and never fully at home there. This section of the book examines man's requirements and explores the difficulties of taking that environment into orbit. While reading the following chapter, it is worth considering how man's preoccupation with staying alive in space could well have an impact on his ability to carry out a military task in space.

10

Man in Space — Physiological Constraints

In the 28 years since the epic flight of Vostok-1, over 200 men and women of 20 nations have spent a total of more than 8,000 man-days in space. And, although NASA was deliberately founded as a civilian organisation for 'the peaceful exploration of space' and *Mir* is the Russian word for peace, it is quite clear that a great many of the man-days achieved have been of a military nature. Physiology and medicine, however, do not recognise such distinctions, and the problems of survival and health which *any* traveller into space must overcome are the same. The continuing success of the manned spaceflight programmes is evidence that, despite a few tragic setbacks, man can be sent into space and returned safely to Earth. Furthermore, Project Apollo demonstrated the ability of man to survive on the surface of another planet, while many of the unique physiological problems associated with prolonged spaceflight have been successfully addressed during the Soviet Soyuz/ Salyut/Mir flights and the American Skylab and Space Transportation System (Shuttle) missions.

The introduction of a human to a spacecraft system is an expensive, complicated and difficult undertaking since all aspects of life and work must be supported as it is on Earth; it matters not whether the work is of a military nature or is benign. Figure 10.1 summarises many of the psycho-physiological inter-relationships between the occupants of a spacecraft and their environment.

Some of the topics listed are obviously of immediate concern to any person who journeys into space, no matter for how short a time, whilst additional aspects confront those embarking upon a prolonged mission. This somewhat artificial distinction provides a useful approach to the subject and is used in this chapter.

PROBLEMS OF IMMEDIATE CONCERN

Decreased Pressure and Density

An exponential fall in atmospheric pressure and density accompanies ascent to altitude so that, for example, ambient pressure at 5,486 metres (18,000 feet) is half that at sea level. By 30,480 metres (100,000 feet), atmospheric pressure is just 1.09 kiloPascals (kPa) (8.2 millimetres Mercury (mmHg)). At such an altitude, although the gaseous composition of air is still the same as it is at sea level (ie, approximately 21 per cent oxygen, 79 per cent nitrogen), its pressure (and specifically that of the

121

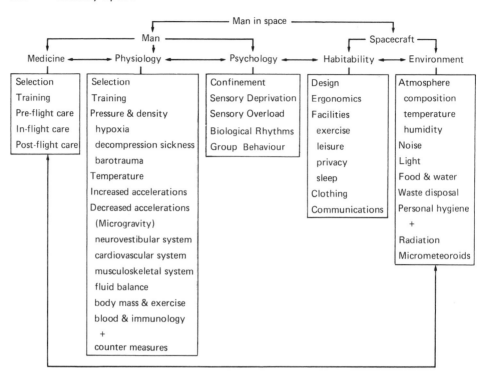

FIG 10.1. Space: Inter-relationships between man and his environment.

oxygen component) is totally inadequate to sustain life. Indeed, this applies to any altitude above about 3,048 metres (10,000 feet). This is because it is the pressure of oxygen in the inspired air which acts as the driving force required to ensure delivery of that gas to all cells of the body. At sea level, the partial pressure of oxygen in the atmosphere is 21.3 kPa (159.6 mmHg) (ie, 21 per cent of 101.3 kPa (760 mmHg)). This pressure has fallen to 13.7 kPa (103 mmHg) by the time the air has reached the lungs as contributions are added from water vapour and carbon dioxide. It is this driving force of 13.7 kPa (103 mmHg) in the lungs which all life support systems for use at altitude strive to maintain.

There is, however, an in-built physiological reserve of some 5.7 kPa (43 mmHg) courtesy of the manner in which oxygen combines with haemoglobin in the red blood cells, and this allows a safe reduction in optimal driving force, for healthy individuals, to about 8.0 kPa (60 mmHg); a level found after an unprotected ascent to 3,048 metres (10,000 feet).

Should the partial pressure of oxygen fall below this value (ie, should ascent to altitudes above 3,047 metres (10,000 feet occur)), the body will be affected by hypoxia (lack of oxygen).

Hypoxia. Hypoxia is the most serious hazard associated with ascent to altitude and produces clinical features of greater severity and with increasing rapidity as altitude increases. Thus, at altitudes of 3,048–4,573 metres (10,000–15,000 feet) subtle disturbances of mental function occur with personality change, euphoria, loss of self-criticism and judgement, loss of short-term memory, and mental incoordination. At altitudes of 4,573–7,620 metres (15,000–25,000 feet), more florid neurological and cardio-respiratory features are seen as compensatory mechanisms manifest. Thus, the special senses (particularly vision and touch) will deteriorate and muscular inco-ordination will develop as the blood supply to less vital organs is diverted to the brain. An increase in the rate and depth of respiration in an attempt to increase oxygen uptake only results in the development of hyperventilation (ie, elimination of too much carbon dioxide), with its additional features of lightheadedness, feelings of unreality, anxiety, pins and needles, and palpitations. This spectrum of symptoms and signs is seen over three to five minutes at an altitude of 7,620 metres (25,000 feet) (although there is considerable variability between individuals), and with increasing severity and rapidity as altitude increases until, if rapid exposure to altitudes above about 13,716 metres (45,000 feet) occurs, unconsciousness within 15 to 20 seconds and death three to four minutes later is inevitable.

Decompression sickness. The fall in total atmospheric pressure which accom-panies ascent to altitude may also produce decompression sickness, another poten-tially fatal condition. In this case, gases dissolved within body fluids come out of solution, or evolve, as surrounding pressure falls, in a manner similar to the appearance of bubbles in a bottle of carbonated drink when the top is removed. If the gas so evolved is also relatively insoluble, as is the case with nitrogen in the human body, it remains in gaseous form and may travel around the body to produce various clinical manifestations according to the site of accumulation. Thus, if the bubbles gather around joints, the classic 'bends' pain may be felt; whilst itching (the 'creeps') and rashes may develop if the skin is affected. If bubbles accumulate in the small blood vessels of the lung, more sinister features develop, with difficulty breathing and a painful cough (the 'chokes'). Similarly, bubbles around the brain and spinal cord may have a devastating effect and produce a wide variety of neurological symptoms and signs (collectively called the 'staggers'), including paralysis and pro-found shock.

The risk of developing decompression sickness is minimal if the (critical) ratio of the initial pressure of nitrogen in the atmosphere to the final total atmospheric pressure is less than 1.5 to 1.8. This means that for healthy individuals starting at sea level, decompression sickness is virtually unknown at altitudes below 5,488 metres (18,000 feet) (critical ratio 1.6), and very rare below 7,622 metres (25,000 feet) (critical ratio 2.1). With increasing altitude above 7,622 metres (25,000 feet), the illness becomes more common and more severe.

Spacecraft and spacesuit pressurisation to a level which would not allow the critical ratio to be exceeded on decompression is one way of reducing the risk, but this is not always technically possible or physiologically desirable (see below). Alternatively, nitrogen can be eliminated from the body entirely, so removing all risk of decom-pression sickness, by pre-breathing 100 per cent oxygen for a period before the proposed decompression (eg, prior to extra-vehicular activity). Both methods are used in manned spaceflight, and protection against decompression sickness is a vital part of the design and function of life support systems in space.

Barotrauma. Gases within body cavities will obey Boyle's Law, which states that at constant temperature, the pressure within such cavities is inversely related to volume. On ascent, therefore, gas which is free to do so will expand as pressure falls, while the increase in pressure on descent will cause a reduction in gas volume. Similar behaviour will occur during pressure changes whilst in space when preparing for suited activities at pressures lower than those of the spacecraft cabin (equivalent to an ascent) or on return (equivalent to a descent).

The gas-containing cavities of concern on ascent are those of the lungs, the gut, and the teeth. Expanding gas in the lungs and the gut, however, vents easily through the trachea (windpipe), and the oesophagus (gullet) or rectum, respectively. Unless a severe decompression occurs, neither organ presents a problem in this respect. Air pockets in diseased teeth, or inadvertently left under the filling in those which have been restored, may give rise to severe pain on ascent as pressure within the pocket increases. Regular dental examination and treatment are therefore essential.

On descent, pressure within the middle ears or sinuses may be unable to equalise with the increasing pressure of the environment because the small openings connecting these cavities (the Eustachian tubes leading from the back of the mouth to the middle ears, and the ostia opening into the nose from the sinuses) with the outside are unable to cope with the pressure change, perhaps because of its rapidity or because of pre-existing illness, such as a cold, which makes the openings prone to closure. Severe pain (barotrauma) in the affected ear or sinus is the result. Although the middle ears may be ventilated by various manual techniques such as pinching the nose and raising the pressure within the mouth, the sinuses cannot be voluntarily relieved in this way. Such barotrauma is therefore avoided as far as possible by grounding any crew member with a cold. Should barotrauma occur in flight, however, the use of nasal decongestants may help.

Thermal Injury. The temperatures to which man may be exposed in space vary enormously depending on the position of the Sun, metabolic activity and the measures adopted to control spacecraft temperature. Since humans are able to survive neither a prolonged fall nor a prolonged rise in body core temperature, protection against the potential range of temperatures ($-113°$ to $+1100$ °C) is an essential and obvious requirement. In fact, the principal problem is that of excessive heat generated by men and equipment within the small volume of a spacecraft cabin and the even smaller volume of a spacesuit. Effective heat dissipation is therefore crucial.

With the exception of their inevitable role in the few fatal accidents, none of these physiological hazards has presented a major problem during the manned missions so far flown because spacecraft Environmental Control (Life Support) Systems provide adequate oxygen at adequate pressure, and maintain the cabin interior at acceptable levels of temperature and humidity. Removal of carbon dioxide and other contaminants from the spacecraft atmosphere is also accomplished by the Environmental Control System.

Spacecraft Environmental Control Systems. Manned spacecraft fly at altitudes where cabin pressurisation in the manner used for conventional aircraft is no longer effective, since compression of air of such low density is both inefficient and uneconomic. Spacecraft cabins are hermetically sealed before flight either at a pressure equivalent to that at sea level or at another selected level. Thereafter, cabin pressure is maintained, and losses through leaks from the cabin to space and from oxygen consumption by the crew are made good, by continual replenishment from stored or generated supplies.

The choice of cabin atmosphere is determined both by engineering and by physiological considerations. Clearly, the physiological ideal would be to provide an atmosphere with the gaseous composition of air at or near sea-level pressure. All Soviet spacecraft have been so equipped, despite the considerable penalties of weight, bulk and complexity which such a system involves. In addition, although pressurisation to sea-level equivalent is physiologically attractive for most spacecraft activities, little protection against the risk of decompression sickness is possible if the cosmonaut wishes to undertake EVA (Extra-Vehicular Activity). A period of pre-oxygenation with 100 per cent oxygen is therefore required before such activity is undertaken, even though Soviet spacesuits are pressurised to a relatively high level (see below).

The Americans have taken a rather different path. Originally, a low-pressure single-gas system was designed which provided a logistically acceptable solution (in terms of weight and bulk) and was relatively simple to engineer (in terms of control mechanisms). For the Mercury, Gemini, Apollo and Skylab programmes, a cabin pressure of 34.5 kPa (259 mmHg) was chosen with a gaseous composition of 100 per cent oxygen. The use of oxygen as the sole breathing gas also eliminated the problem of decompression sickness, provided that pre-oxygenation before flight was adequate. Pure oxygen at a pressure of 34.5 kPa (259 mmHg) is below any directly toxic threshold for oxygen, so long-term use was thought unlikely to be harmful. But there remained a reduced margin of safety in the event of loss of cabin pressurisation, an additional heat load on the cooling system by virtue of poor heat conduction in a low-density gas, and of course a great risk of explosion and fire.

Projects Mercury and Gemini were completed using the single-gas (oxygen) system, but the death of the crew of Test Apollo 204 in 1967 in an oxygen-fuelled flash fire led to a redesign for later missions. A two-gas system was introduced in order to reduce the fire hazard during the critical launch period. Thus, for all Apollo and Skylab flights, a mixture of 36 per cent oxygen and 64 per cent nitrogen was used to pressurise the cabin at 101.3 kPa (760 mmHg) for launch. The pressure was reduced to 34.5 kPa (259 mmHg) within a few hours of launch and nitrogen was gradually purged from the cabin so that the atmosphere was approximately 95 per cent oxygen 5 per cent nitrogen for Apollo, and 70 per cent oxygen 30 per cent nitrogen for Skylab. Since, at 25.5 kPa (191 mmHg), spacesuit pressure was close to cabin pressure for these flights, no pre-oxygenation was required prior to EVA.

The Shuttle is the first American spacecraft to utilise an atmosphere of sea-level composition and pressure. Any EVA during Shuttle missions is therefore preceded by a period of pre-oxygenation. In order to reduce the time necessary for adequate pre-oxygenation, which would otherwise be operationally unacceptably long, the whole cabin undergoes an intermediate decompression to 70.2 kPa (527 mmHg). The entire crew then breathes 27 per cent oxygen for 12 hours before the two astronauts destined to leave the craft breathe 100 per cent oxygen for 40 minutes.

In order to avoid serious disturbances of physiology and performance, the concentration of carbon dioxide in inspired gas must also be strictly controlled. Safe design levels for the partial pressure of carbon dioxide in both Soviet and American spacecraft have been set at about 0.5 kPa (4 mmHg), with a maximum limit for continuous exposure of 1.0 kPa (7.6 mmHg). Levels have usually been controlled to well below this, however, at about 0.13 kPa (1 mmHg). Chemical scrubbers are used to remove carbon dioxide in Soviet craft, while lithium hydroxide cannisters have been used in all American craft except Skylab where a molecular sieve was employed.

Other chemical and biological cabin contaminants, including those from the environmental control system itself, waste management systems, spacecraft materials and paints, and indeed crew members, must also be dealt with. This is usually and effectively accomplished by circulating the cabin air through activated charcoal filters.

Finally, spacecraft environmental control systems control temperature and humidity. The principal problem of thermal control within spacecraft and spacesuits has always been that of heat dissipation from various engineering systems and from body metabolism. Within the range 10–32 °C, control has been successfully achieved by a variety of conventional heat dissipation mechanisms including sublimation, evaporation, radiation, and liquid-air heat exchange. Likewise, control of cabin humidity has been achieved by the use of sophisticated water extractors; once again, the main problem is that of water excess from metabolic production. Cabin relative humidity has been controlled over the ranges 40–70 per cent (Soviet craft) and 30–70 per cent (American craft).

Spacesuits and Portable Life Support Systems. A spacesuit provides the means by which it is possible to venture outside a spacecraft either in free space or on the surface of another planet. It also provides a refuge within a spacecraft in the event of an on-board emergency. In its simplest form, a spacesuit consists of an inner rubber bladder to hold gas under pressure and an outer restraining layer which prevents ballooning and allows movement. Gas for suit pressurisation is delivered to or contained within the bladder, and other vital supplies such as a breathable atmosphere suitably cooled and humidified, and a supply of water, must also be delivered. Carbon dioxide must also be scrubbed from the breathing circuit. While the wearer remains dependent on the mother ship, such facilities may be conveniently provided via an umbilical. When the user must be entirely independent of his spacecraft, all the supporting facilities are self-contained and constitute a PLSS (Portable Life Support System); only the need for food may reasonably be omitted from such a system, although the management of solid and liquid waste must still be considered.

The spacesuits worn by Vostok cosmonauts and Mercury astronauts were virtually identical to the full-pressure suits used by pilots of high-altitude military aircraft. With later programmes came the requirement to operate beyond the confines of the spacecraft so, while basic suit function remained the same, several specialised features were introduced, including the extensive use of layering (for thermal and micrometeoroid protection), the introduction of technology to improve joint mobility, the incorporation of special helmets, gloves and boots, and the evolution of sophisticated PLSSs.

PLATE 10.1. Untethered astronaut operating independently from his spacecraft; he relies completely upon his Portable Life Support System (*NASA*)

A typical American PLSS, as used for the Apollo lunar landing missions, comprised five main sub-systems, all housed in a back-pack and supplying the suit itself via a series of short umbilicals. The primary oxygen system provided breathing gas from a gaseous store and also pressurised the suit and helmet to 25.5 kPa (191 mmHg). Higher pressurisation, while physiologically more desirable, would have reduced mobility to an unacceptable degree. Soviet spacesuit technology is more advanced in this respect since good mobility is retained despite pressurisation to 40.0 kPa (300 mmHg). A ventilating system circulated and purified the oxygen by passing it through lithium hydroxide to absorb carbon dioxide, and through a filter to remove trace contaminants. Cooling was accomplished by a porous plate sublimator and any excess water from respiration and perspiration was removed by a water separator. The third major sub-system was a water transport loop which removed metabolic heat by circulating chilled water through the network of plastic pipes which made up the liquid-cooling garment. This system enabled very high metabolic rates to be sustained for several hours while the average metabolic rate for lunar activities could be tolerated for eight hours: the maximum duration of the PLSS main oxygen supply. An independent, manually operated, oxygen purge system provided an emergency breathing and pressurisation supply for up to 40 minutes should the main supply be exhausted or in the event of loss of suit pressure. The fifth sub-system comprised the communications and biotelemetry facilities. Two-way voice transmission was supplemented by physiological and spacesuit environmental data such as electrocardiograph, oxygen supply and suit pressures, and water inlet and outlet temperatures. Analysis of these data allowed a rough estimate of metabolic oxygen consumption and energy expenditure to be derived which, when compared with measurements obtained pre-flight, ensured that each astronaut was kept within the safety limits of his oxygen supply and heat removal systems.

Increased Accelerations. Acceleration (or deceleration) is a force, and is defined as the rate of change of velocity with time. For most people on Earth, the acceleration due to gravity, experienced as weight, is the only such force encountered throughout their lives, although small changes in the magnitude of this acceleration occur every time there is a change in the speed or direction of motion of the body. Military pilots and astronauts, however, are exposed to much greater accelerations as part of their normal occupation.

The magnitude of such increased accelerations is conventionally expressed as multiples of the normal acceleration due to gravity. Thus, when a pilot states that he is 'in a 4G turn', he is indicating that his aircraft is accelerating at a force four times that of normal gravity. Subjectively, he will feel four times heavier than normal. With respect to the human body, acceleration acting from head to foot is described as +Gz (positive) acceleration, while that acting from foot to head is −Gz (negative). Similarly, +Gx describes chest-to-back acceleration, and −Gx describes back-to-chest. And +Gy and −Gy describe left-to-right and right-to-left accelerations, respectively. Since man is ordinarily an upright animal, it is the z axis which is of particular concern in flight.

When exposed in a centrifuge to increased +Gz accelerations, a relaxed, unprotected, seated subject will usually lose consciousness by about +6Gz, although other factors such as the rate of onset, height of the subject and previous experience will all modify this point. If the rate of onset is sufficiently slow, a clearly defined sequence of events will precede loss of consciousness. Thus, at +2Gz, there is a subjective feeling of increased weight with drooping of soft body tissues, especially of the face. By +2.5Gz it is extremely difficult to lift from the seat and at +3 to +4Gz it is impossible. At about +3.5Gz, there is progressive dimming of the visual fields (greyout) with loss of peripheral vision. Vision then fails completely (blackout) although consciousness and mental function is retained. Unconsciousness then ensues, frequently with accompanying convulsions. There is also difficulty breathing, and cramps and congestion of the lower limbs. All these changes are the consequence of the cardiovascular effects of acceleration, and specifically the alteration in normal pressure gradients throughout the body. Positive Gz acceleration will reduce effective pressure above the heart and increase it below that level, so that perfusion of the brain fails while the lower body is engorged.

Even if protective manoeuvres are used, such as straining and muscle tensing, and protective devices such as G-trousers, positive-pressure breathing and reclined seats, the most highly trained and fit pilots will be able to tolerate only +10 to +12Gz for less than 60 seconds. And –Gz is even less tolerable for normal human subjects.

Acceleration in the Gx axis is, however, better tolerated, and is primarily limited by effects on the chest and lungs (rather than on the brain). At +2 to +3Gx, there is a feeling of increased weight and abdominal pressure, but +2Gx is tolerable for at least 24 hours. In the range of accelerations seen during spacecraft launches (+3 to +9Gx—see below), there is increasingly severe chest pain with difficulty breathing and speaking as a result of the increased weight of the chest. The human limit to +Gx acceleration comes at +15Gx with vice-like chest pain, loss of sensation, vision and then consciousness. Although the effects are similar during –Gx acceleration, reversal of the force vector makes breathing easier.

The velocities required for a spacecraft to achieve Earth orbit or Earth escape may be reached by any number of combinations of acceleration and time provided that their product is 828 G-seconds for the former and 1,152 G-seconds for the latter. The magnitude of spacecraft acceleration is, however, determined by constraints on rocket design and performance so that, in practice, a staged launch is used to achieve the final velocity required. Thus, for example, a two-stage acceleration profile of 6.0G for 35 seconds followed by 6.4G for 54 seconds with peaks of 8.0G was used for a Mercury–Atlas orbital launch. Subsequent American and Soviet launch profiles have been somewhat less severe with little time spent above 4.0G even for the Apollo lunar missions. With the exception of the conventional return of the American Shuttle and Soviet orbiter, spacecraft re-entry accelerations have occasionally been considerably more severe with an average maximum of up to 10.0G for Vostok, 8.9G for Mercury, and 5.9G for Apollo. Voskhod and Soyuz re-entry profiles have an average maximum of 4.0G.

Levels of acceleration such as these will clearly have profound physiological effects and will be poorly tolerated unless applied transversely; that is, in the Gx (chest-back) axis. Body orientation has therefore been in that axis, with the accelerative forces acting in the +Gx (backward) direction during launch and the –Gx axis (chestward) during re-entry. The exception is the +Gz orientation of returning Shuttle crews who are exposed to just +1.2 Gz during re-entry, although the duration of this applied force is 17 minutes and may have physiologically significant effects after even a short period in microgravity.

Landing shock imposes a final increased acceleration to the returning crewman. The Soviet programme has consistently called for landings on to solid ground while, until the reusable Shuttle flights, the Americans chose water. In both cases, retardation of the space capsule is achieved by parachutes deployed at an altitude of about 9,144 metres (30,000 feet). Exceptions to this are the orbiter craft with their runway return, and Vostok from which the occupant was obliged to eject.

Radiation

Most electromagnetic radiation coming from space is either shielded by the Earth's atmospheric blanket or is deflected by its magnetic field. Spacecraft, by definition, travel beyond these protective layers so they, and their occupants, are exposed to the full power of the electromagnetic spectrum and especially of ionising radiations.

Ionising Radiations. Ionising radiation from space is termed cosmic radiation and its two main types bombard the Earth continuously. The first, galactic cosmic radiation, originates from beyond the solar system and produces a steady and fairly predictable low-intensity flux of high-energy particles. This stream is attenuated by the deflecting action of the Earth's magnetic field and by absorption within the upper atmosphere. The magnetic field is most potent at the equator, but its influence diminishes to almost zero at the Poles, while atmospheric absorption declines as altitude increases. Although solar cosmic radiation, the second main type, consists of low-energy particles, it may occasionally be produced with such high intensity that even the upper layers of the atmosphere are penetrated.

Once in space, of course, the protection of the Earth's magnetic field and atmosphere is lost and both galactic radiation and, particularly, solar radiation provide a serious threat to the health of the space traveller.

In addition, two further sources of ionising radiation must be considered. The first is the trapped radiation found within the two bands of geomagnetically held high-energy particles which form the Van Allen belts. The inner belt lies at an altitude of 241–965 km depending on latitude, while the outer belt begins at 7,966 km and may extend as high as 43,853 km. Most manned space activities now take place well below the inner belt, so ionising radiation from these sources presents no major problem, although it was of potential concern for the Apollo lunar missions and would be of concern for craft in high Earth orbit. Unfortunately, there is also a discontinuity in the Earth's magnetic field over the South Atlantic (the South Atlantic Anomaly) and here the particles of the inner Van Allen belt can be detected at altitudes as low as 129–257 km. The implications for spacecraft such as Salyut, Mir, the Shuttle and the Soviet orbiter when operating in low Earth orbit in this region are clear and EVA should be avoided during such times.

The second additional type of ionising radiation is the energetic neutron. Such neutrons are probably formed within spacecraft as secondary radiation when internal components are bombarded by primary radiation from, for example, the Van Allen belts. Energetic neutrons are potentially very dangerous since they cause disruption of biological tissue when they collide with hydrogen nuclei.

Although radiation in space can take many forms, it should be regarded as a single threat; and indeed it is considered by many to be *the* principal hazard for prolonged orbital and interplanetary spaceflight.

Biological Effects of Ionising Radiation. Ionising radiation disrupts all living tissue at the cellular level and devastates crucial cell components with remarkable speed. For obvious reasons, descriptions of the biological effects of ionising radiation on man have largely been based on clinical studies of acutely ill individuals and it is therefore unwise to extrapolate such findings to the healthy space traveller. Furthermore, some types of ionising radiation experienced in space are unique to that environment. But Earth-based medical experience currently provides the best indication of the effects likely to be seen in space. The clinical effects of *acute* exposure to ionising radiation range from minor blood changes seen after low-dose exposures, to prolonged vomiting and nausea with many fatalities over months, weeks and days as the dose level increases, and then to incapacitation and death within hours or minutes at very high doses. Such a spectrum of illness reflects in part the progressive influence radiation has on the most sensitive body tissues, ie, those which are most actively growing—new blood elements and the lining of the gut. Based on intelligent interpretation of these clinical data, the levels of radiation above which astronauts and cosmonauts should not be *chronically* exposed can be predicted, and limits imposed upon total time spent in space. For example, NASA imposes a career limitation on astronauts of cumulative long-term doses of radiation to the bone marrow, the lens of the eye, and to the skin. The doses vary for each tissue according to its particular sensitivity to radiation. Career limitations of this sort have determined that flights on board the proposed International Space Station for a career astronaut will be a maximum of 90 to 120 days. The Soviet attitude is slightly different in that the current policy of its manned spaceflight programme appears to be to allow a cosmonaut a maximum of just three or four flights in a career.

Protection Against Ionising Radiations. Radiation levels are monitored routinely on board all Soviet and American spacecraft; passive dosimeters are used to record cumulative exposure and active pocket dosimeters are used to assess immediate risks. During the prolonged occupations of the Skylab, Salyut and Mir space stations, no dangerously high levels of ionising radiation were encountered within the craft, and throughout the manned programmes EVAs were avoided if any increase in solar flare activity was predicted or detected. But the very long missions planned for the future will pose a much increased risk and this is why radiation effects are regarded so seriously. The passive shielding against ionising radiation by physical means has been effective so far but a limit exists for the thickness of a physical barrier (a lead shield one metre thick would be needed to provide protection around a spacecraft equivalent to that of the Earth's atmosphere). For the future, therefore, active methods, perhaps by inducing a magnetic field around an individual spacecraft or perhaps by pharmacological means, may have to be considered.

Micrometeoroids

Micrometeoroids are small particles of solid matter, usually made of stone and/or iron, which form interplanetary dust. Vast quantities of this material is present throughout the galaxy, and indeed over 10,000 tonnes of it survives the passage through the atmosphere each day to fall on the Earth's surface. The particles are usually very small but may be of sufficient energy to form craters in, but not to penetrate, metal sheets. The conventional walls of a spacecraft thus form an effective passive shield against impacts of this nature. Whilst undertaking EVA, however, the risk increases, albeit slightly, and hence there is a need to incorporate suitable layers of protective material within a spacesuit.

PLATE 10.2. Fresh food for the STS. Fresh food now forms a routine element of a space diet, but this was not always the case (*NASA*)

Food and Water, Waste Management, and Personal Hygiene

Food. The metabolic requirements for food in space were initially based on values from Earthbound studies of the energy cost of various activities. Confirmation of the requirements was obtained from in-flight studies as the manned spaceflight programmes progressed. Thus, for example, the early Soyuz cosmonauts received a daily caloric (energy) intake of 2,800 kcal but this had risen to 3,150 kcal by the time of the Salyut 6 flights. Similarly, the American daily allowance has risen from 2,500 kcal during early projects to 3,000 kcal on board Skylab and the Shuttle, reflecting the intense physical activity undertaken on those missions. Essential nutritional needs, such as vitamins, amino acids, and the balance between fats, carbohydrates and sugars, were also derived from terrestrial studies.

The manner in which food is presented in space has undergone considerable (and necessary) refinement throughout the manned spaceflight programmes. Early space food was provided as somewhat unappetising purees and juices contained like toothpaste in soft metal tubes. Food technology has advanced considerably, however, and crews are now able to pre-select meals from a large menu of foodstuffs, both fresh and preserved, in a variety of ways such as freeze-dried, thermostabilised, and rehydratable.

Water. For all Soviet missions, water has been carried as a potable supply prepared on Earth. The recommended total daily intake for cosmonauts, as water and in food, is about two and a half litres for the relatively benign missions within spacecraft, but twice this amount if EVA is undertaken. Similarly, all supplies were pre-loaded in American spacecraft until the introduction of electrical fuel cells as a power source and the ability to purify the water generated as a by-product in that process. A daily consumption of about three litres is recommended for astronauts.

Waste Management. The satisfactory disposal of human waste products is clearly a vital aspect of life support engineering in space. Carbon dioxide and water vapour are satisfactorily dealt with by the environmental control systems, but the management of urine and faeces has presented considerable problems.

All Soviet spacecraft have been equipped with waste disposal ventilators, rather like vacuum cleaners, which are able to draw off urine and faeces simultaneously, and can be used even when a spacesuit is being worn. This level of sophistication was not achieved in the American programme until the flights of Skylab and the Shuttle. In earlier programmes, urine was initially collected by means of a roll-on rubber cuff connected to tubing for delivery either to a flexible plastic bag or to the overboard dumping system. This method was relatively simple and effective, but regarded as unhygienic. For later missions, a hand-held receptacle was provided into which urine was voided, so removing the need for intimate contact. Disposal of solid waste when on board early American spacecraft was by means of the universally detested 'faecal mit'. This device consisted of a finger cot and plastic bag with a self-adhesive orifice which was applied to the anal area. After use, which was a considerable accomplishment within the confines of a small but public spacecraft and took approximately 45 minutes, the bag was sealed and its contents mixed by hand with a bacteriocidal liquid before being stored for later analysis. Defecation when inside a spacesuit was even more basic; not surprisingly, there is no record of the spacesuit faecal containment system, which was really an adult nappy, ever having been used.

Personal Hygiene. Human beings usually like both themselves and their surroundings to be clean and tidy, an aspect of living in space which is as important psychologically, in terms of maintenance of morale, as it is medically, in terms of maintenance of good health. Consequently, the need for adequate facilities and materials for the maintenance of oral hygiene, for the cleansing of skin, and for the disposal of other less obvious forms of human waste such as hair and nails has always been recognised as vital. And time spent dealing with these aspects forms a very important part of the ritual of life on board spacecraft.

The daily input and output for the average human body is summarised in Figure 10.2.

Living in space			
Daily input		Daily output	
Food	0.7 kg	Faeces	0.2 kg
Water: Potable	2 - 4 kg	Urine	2 - 3 kg
: Washing	1.5 kg	Flatus	0.5 L
Oxygen	0.9 kg	Carbon dioxide	0.8 kg
		Skin	8 g

Hair grows at 0.35 mm.d^{-1}
Nails grow at 0.1 to 0.2 mm.d^{-1}

FIG 10.2. The daily input and output for the average human body.

LONG-TERM PROBLEMS

Decreased Acceleration—Microgravity

Although very brief periods of microgravity are experienced during violent and unnatural manoeuvres in high-performance military aircraft, the phenomenon as it affects human physiology is essentially exclusive to the environment of space.

The term microgravity is used in preference to the more familiar 'weightlessness' because, since the force of gravity decreases with the inverse square of the distance from the Earth's centre, some gravitational attraction will always be present (although its intensity may be very small) until the influence of another planetary body is entered. Thus, even in deep space, conditions of zero gravity do not exist; the occupants of spacecraft are normally exposed to a micro-gravity of 1×10^{-4} to 1×10^{-5} G, rising to 1×10^{-3} G during spacecraft manoeuvres.

A spacecraft and its occupants, once in orbit above the effective limits of the atmosphere, are in a state of free-fall about the Earth because of the continuous accelerative force of gravity pulling towards the centre of the planet. The craft does not fall back to Earth for as long as orbital velocity is maintained because the resultant tangential and inertial forces exactly counterbalance the force of gravity. When this state of equilibrium is achieved, the spacecraft and its crew are in microgravity.

While certain techniques, such as suspension in water at neutral buoyancy and prolonged bed-rest, have proved successful in providing partial models (and have been helpful in training in techniques of movement and of equipment utilisation), microgravity cannot really be simulated adequately in a laboratory on Earth. The principal reason for this is that essentially normal proprioceptive function is retained in the 1 G environment. Furthermore, the duration of microgravity generated by Keplerian (parabolic) flight trajectories in large aircraft is too short (at 12–40 seconds) to provide any valuable physiological model, but again has been useful for familiarisation training of crews prior to space missions. In addition, all such terrestrially based experiments do provide at least some clues to the physiological mechanisms invoked by exposure to microgravity.

PLATE 10.3. Physiology in space. The physiological problems of microgravity are best studied by in-flight experimentation (*NASA*)

Elucidation of human physiology in microgravity has therefore had to rely on spaceflight experience. Initially, studies of human function were made purely in support of the operational requirements of the early manned spaceflight programmes of Vostok, Voskhod, Mercury and Gemini, and continued throughout Project Apollo. It was not until the scientific missions of Skylab, Salyut, Shuttle and Mir that detailed and dedicated physiological investigations were undertaken. Even then, it must be emphasised that the total number of experiments remains small, the sample population is likewise small and highly selected, the potential benefit of any countermeasure has led to its use despite a lack of supporting evidence, and the operational requirements of a mission have always, quite correctly, held sway over the wishes of investigators.

The Physiological Consequences of Microgravity

The manned spaceflight programmes have conclusively demonstrated that it is possible to work and live effectively in space for days, weeks and months despite conditions of microgravity. Microgravity does, however, produce marked changes in all areas of physiology, changes which are of vital importance to the success of the prolonged missions planned for the future since a safe return to Earth depends on their reversal. Microgravity principally affects the physiology of the neuro-vestibular system, the cardiovascular system, and the musculo-skeletal system.

Neuro-vestibular System. Space motion sickness is part of the Space Adaptation Syndrome and is the most important vestibular consequence of spaceflight, affecting as it does over 45 per cent of crew members in the current generation of large spacecraft. The term 'sickness' is really a misnomer since the phenomenon is the normal response of a healthy neuro-vestibular system. Cosmonaut Titov, the second Soviet in space, was the first to report symptoms during his flight in Vostok 2, but American astronauts were unaffected until the Apollo programme because the ability to make body and head movements in the Mercury and Gemini capsules was limited.

The cause of space motion sickness is believed to be the same as that of its terrestrial equivalents: when exposed to a sickness-inducing environment (such as wave motion on ships, air turbulence in aircraft, or lack of gravity in space) the signals received from the special senses (vision, balance and position) by the brain are at variance with those expected and normally received in a stable 1-G state. The brain responds to this mismatch by inducing the familiar features of the syndrome: pallor, sweating, nausea and vomiting. In space, these features appear in crew members within hours of entry to microgravity and consequently at a potentially vital operational stage. Incapacitation for this reason is therefore a very serious problem, and one for which active treatment is required.

Unfortunately, there is as yet no way of predicting the likelihood of susceptibility before flight: and apparent immunity to Earth-based motion sickness may confer no protection in space. Those identified as susceptible (and not all those affected are identified before a mission) are given preventative (prophylactic) anti-sickness drugs; those stricken once in orbit also receive drugs. Other techniques known to help the sufferer is to keep as still as possible (usually by being wedged into a corner) and for the rest of the crew to remain in the same 'upright' orientation as the victim; to see people floating upside-down is not conducive to rapid recovery. Space motion sickness invariably resolves (usually within two to four days) as the neuro-vestibular system adapts to microgravity. But it is precisely those first few days which may be of the greatest operational importance to a military mission; hence the very active research programmes directed towards more effective solutions.

Other effects of microgravity on the neuro-vestibular system include in-flight illusions of orientation (manifest particularly, for example, on awakening to see a colleague sleeping inverted), and bizarre post-flight illusory phenomena described by some returning astronauts.

Cardiovascular System. Microgravity neutralises pressure gradients within the circulation and the consequent uniformity (particularly of venous pressures) causes a headward shift of up to two litres of fluid which is complete within one to two days. The subjective effects of such a shift include persistent sensations of nasal stuffiness and feelings of fullness in the head. The veins of the head and neck are visibly distended and remain so throughout flight.

The expansion of central (ie, thoracic) fluid volume in this way causes hormonal changes which stimulate excretion of urine. Virtually all cosmonauts and astronauts have indeed lost weight during spaceflight, but the early phase of this loss is mainly attributable to suppression of thirst and only partially to the increased urine output. For example, when compared with pre-flight values, each Skylab astronaut excreted about 400 millilitres less urine daily over the first six days of flight, and drank an average of 700 millilitres less each day. On-board measurements of body mass reflected this fluid imbalance as a rapid loss of 1–2 kg within three or four days, followed by a steady but slower fall during the rest of the flight due to loss of muscle (as a result of atrophy (wasting)) and fat (as a result of sub-optimal caloric intake).

The most important consequence of fluid redistribution is the development of orthostatic intolerance (ie, a tendency to faint) when blood pools in the legs on return to the 1-G environment of Earth. Symptoms of an impending faint are experienced and there is a reduction in exercise tolerance for several hours post-flight. The development and severity of this cardiovascular deconditioning has been assessed in flight, and results suggest that deterioration does not progress after two to three months in space. No countermeasures so far adopted by either the Soviets or Americans, including the use of anti-G trousers inflated before re-entry to reduce peripheral pooling, and saline ingestion, have been entirely successful. The production of artificial gravity may be the only definitive solution to cardiovascular deconditioning in microgravity.

Musculo-skeletal System. Artificial gravity is also likely to be the only solution to the profound problems of muscle wasting (atrophy) and bone demineralisation seen as a consequence of prolonged exposure to microgravity.

Microgravity reduces the muscular effort required for physical activities and for maintenance of posture. It is therefore not surprising that atrophy of anti-gravity muscle groups occurs, primarily in the legs but also in the buttocks and trunk. The arm muscles are least affected because everyday tasks in space require considerable use of the arms. Rigorous exercise regimes have been shown to reduce the degree of atrophy; such activity is now an essential part of life on board spacecraft and occupies a considerable amount of time. Despite such measures, however, skeletal muscle atrophy leads to a prolonged reduction in post-flight physical work capacity. Of concern also is the recent finding from animal studies that heart muscle may atrophy.

Bone demineralisation, similar to that seen in osteoporosis of the elderly on Earth, probably represents *the* most serious consequence for man of exposure to microgravity since bones so affected are very prone to fracture. There is an inexorable regional loss of bone, with greater losses from the internal supporting material than from the outer, solid, cortex. The loss is reflected in a negative calcium balance which, in Skylab, was characterised by increased losses in the urine and faeces. Although similar metabolic changes are seen in bed-rest and immobilisation studies, the precise mechanisms involved during spaceflight are as yet unclear. Dietary manipulation and exercise regimes appear to have little or no effect in slowing the process.

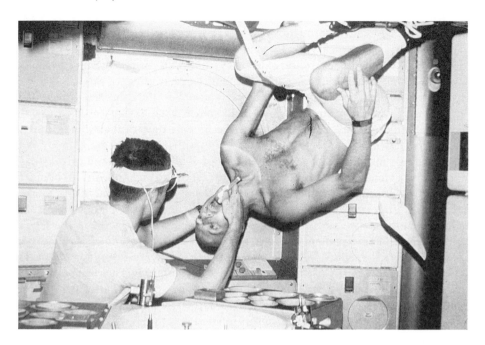

PLATE 10.4. Health care in space. Medical and dental care are vital aspects of life in space.
Here a dental examination on board Skylab is facilitated by microgravity. (*NASA*)

Consequently, it is vital that the condition is understood, and prophylaxis or treatment defined, so that future long-duration missions and subsequent return to Earth may be safely undertaken.

Behavioural Aspects of Manned Spaceflight

Until the advent of the Shuttle with its crews of pilot astronauts, mission specialists and payload specialists, manned spaceflight had been the almost exclusive preserve of military and civilian male test pilots. The crews of early spacecraft were highly selected, highly motivated and highly trained individuals for whom spaceflight alone was achievement enough. As the manned spaceflight programmes progress, it is clear that the crews of future spacecraft will comprise individuals of both sexes, from disparate backgrounds and disciplines, with varying motivating drives, and of different ethnic origins. It is inevitable, therefore, that greater attention must be paid to the psycho-physiological or behavioural aspects of spaceflight (see Figure 10.1). Furthermore, as flights become longer, both in duration and distance travelled from Earth, spacecraft habitability will require further and greater consideration. It will no longer be acceptable to consider manned spaceflight as a challenge just to aeronautical engineering.

Finally, Figure 10.1 lists several other areas of great importance but which it has not been possible to address here. These areas include, especially, selection and training, medical selection and training, and the provision of pre-flight, in-flight, and post-flight health care. It has also not been possible to deal in detail with develop-

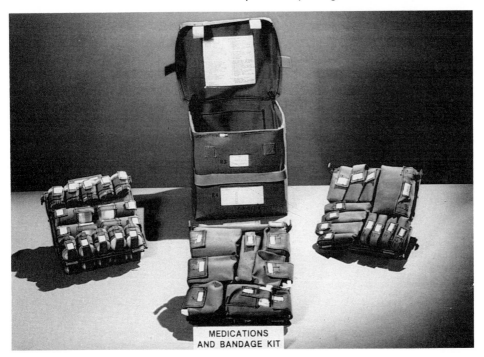

PLATE 10.5. First aid kits. Medical training and provision of equipment are essential for all manned missions. (*NASA*)

ments particularly vital to the future of man in space such as the provision of closed life support systems and artificial gravity.

Space Control

Space Control

Both the United States and the Soviet Union are now heavily dependent on the use of spacecraft in their military operations. First, their craft provide them with their respective means of global communications and navigation. Also meteorological and military surveillance data from all parts of the electromagnetic spectrum are gathered from space on an almost continuous basis. Therefore, the use of spacecraft in any major military operation has effectively become essential for both of the Superpowers. Because of this importance, each power's space assets must be protected from any potential aggressor. Such protection can only be given if military control is exercised over space itself. Here, the word 'control' is used in the same sense as a navy tries to exercise control of the sea, making it an accessible and safe place for friendly forces to operate, while at the same time denying its use to any hostile forces.

The first question to be asked in an analysis of space control is, 'What constitutes a threat in space?' At present there is no evidence of orbiting nuclear weapons or space mines, but a satellite's threat value need not be quite so overt. On the one hand a surveillance satellite could clearly be a threat if it were able to report force dispositions but, on the other hand, are the opposition's navigation satellites a threat? Well, yes they are if those satellites provide the high navigation accuracy for ICBMs or bombers. Similarly, communication satellites could be considered a threat because of their extremely high importance in strategic communication links. As stated at the outset, the use of spacecraft in major military operations is now essential for success. Therefore the success of the operations on Earth could well hinge on the importance of the military satellites. All military satellites are therefore a threat, and a major one at that.

Space control is one of the most complex and costly tasks any nation could hope to accomplish, so for now it is the concern of only the United States and the Soviet Union. Within the overall task, several areas can be identified which will now be analysed separately, although in reality they exist together as an integrated whole.

This section of the book will begin by examining the problems of keeping track of the threat, using surveillance sensors on the Earth. Second, in the chapter on space warfare, the current and future military techniques of active space control are examined, including some of the latest SDI technology. In essence, the chapter covers the classical military concepts of negation of the threat and denial of access to the enemy.

11

The Surveillance of Space

NEED FOR SPACE SURVEILLANCE

Any country or power wishing to exercise military control of space needs a detailed intelligence picture of all the objects in space which pose a potential threat. Because of the high orbital speeds of satellites and their truly global cover, it is pointless to be concerned only with the area of space directly above one's own country. In practical terms, one must have intelligence on the complete space situation because nearly all the satellites will pass over any country sooner or later. The problem is further complicated because of the sheer number of objects orbiting the Earth. The relatively few potential threats in orbit at any time are orbiting along with around 7,000 other large objects comprising friendly, commercial or neutral satellites, dead payloads, rocket upper stages and orbiting debris. Just to complicate things further still, ICBMs en route to a target could easily be mistaken for satellites in orbit because, at apogee, those missiles can rise as high as 1,000 to 1,500 km into space. So clearly, a sophisticated and large network of space-looking intelligence gathering sensors is needed to provide and maintain not only a full picture but also the ability to spot instantly any new threats which appear over the horizon. The space tracking networks of the two Superpowers are therefore closely integrated with their BMEWS (Ballistic Missile Early Warning Systems).

MAJOR FUNCTIONS

Military space surveillance falls, broadly, into five essential functions. First, when an object is launched into space, the system must detect the launch. Then, having detected the launch the object must be tracked, initially to check for a possible ICBM trajectory, but then if the object enters orbit it must be tracked for the first few orbits to establish the orbital parameters. Time and considerable effort will then be expended in identifying the type and role of the satellite. Once the orbital parameters have been sufficiently refined, the object will be catalogued in the space surveillance database. Then, for the rest of the object's orbital life, its orbital parameters must be checked at periodic intervals and the database updated. The database must always be as current as possible so that new events or changes will quickly stand out from the overall picture. Each of the five surveillance functions (detecting, tracking, identifying, cataloguing, and maintaining positional information on all

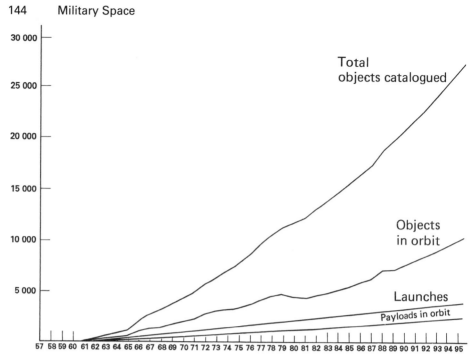

FIG 11.1. The number of trackable objects in space.

man-made objects in space) is sufficiently important in its own right that the techniques and equipment used at each stage deserve separate consideration.

Launch Detection

Of course many launches are publicised well in advance by the nations conducting the launches. However, in those instances when launches are not pre-announced, the first detection of launch will probably be by the US or Soviet launch-detection satellites. These satellites were discussed more fully in Chapter 8; suffice it to say that these launch detection systems will pinpoint the launch site and report the launch within a minute or two of the event. They do not, however, estimate orbital parameters or impact points in the case of ICBMs. This task is left to the fixed radar sites of the BMEWS systems.

As the launchers rise to orbital heights they will almost certainly be detected by the powerful detection radars which serve the dual BMEWS/Space Surveillance roles. Not surprisingly, the systems used by both Superpowers are similar.

Space Vehicle Tracking

The work-horses of the space surveillance radar networks are the phased array radars. Their 10-storey radar antennas, which search space, do not move; instead, their radar beams are formed and scanned by changing the electrical phase of the signals in each of the several thousand small antennas which make up the large array. Each face can form many beams and so focus its energy into several directions at any one time. Also, it can switch targets in a few thousandths of a second. Effec-

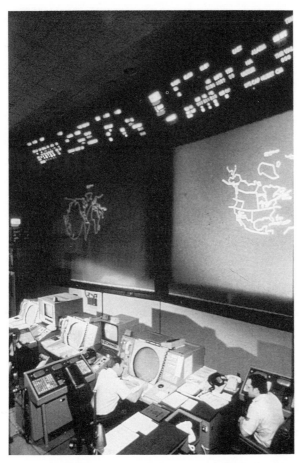

PLATE 11.1. The heart of the Western BMEWS system, NORAD (North American Air Defense Command) Command Post in the Cheyenne Mountain Complex, Colorado Springs, USA. (*USAF Photo*)

tively, therefore, a phased array can track many hundreds of objects at the same time, so it can maintain its major time-consuming task of space tracking without dropping the primary task of ICBM/SLBM warning.

Typically, a phased array such as the US system at Thule, Greenland, has a range of around 4,500 km and can look from three degrees to 85 degrees above the horizon. Each array can look over 120 degrees in azimuth, so it is common to see three of these giant radars, one mounted on each face of a triangular building, to give all-round cover, looking something like a space-age pyramid. In both the United States and the Soviet Union, these phased arrays are replacing the older and much less capable 'radar fan' BMEWS radars which date back to the 1960s.

The prime role of the phased arrays is to give early ICBM or SLBM warning. This is true for both the US and Soviet systems, so the phased arrays are generally located around the edges of the Superpowers' borders and configured to face the probable threat directions. Such a location policy is entirely sensible for the missile warning

PLATE 11.2. The main operations room at RAF Fylingdales BMEWS site, UK. (*Photo: Squadron Leader J Broughton, RAF Fylingdales*)

PLATE 11.3. BMEWS tracking radars at Clear, Alaska. Such older systems are now being replaced by the much more capable phased array systems. (*USAF Photo*)

PLATE 11.4. The Pave Paws phased array radar at Eldorado Air Force Station, Texas.
(*Raytheon*)

tasks but for the space-tracking task it means that extra sensors are needed elsewhere in the world to give full global coverage. For just this purpose, the United States uses large mechanical tracker radars which have steerable parabaloid antennas. These mechanical trackers are located carefully to observe the early orbital periods of launches from the Soviet Union. Such radars are located in the United States, Turkey and at sites in the Atlantic and Pacific oceans. They can all track objects in low Earth orbit but the radars at Pirinclik (Turkey), Roi-Namur (Marshall Islands) and Millstone Hill (USA) can track satellites out at geosynchronous altitude (36,000 km).

The United States also has a unique space radar surveillance system known as the NAVSPASUR (Naval Space Surveillance System), which uses radar interferometery techniques to fix and track satellites as they pass the southern United States. The NAVSPASUR fence, as it is sometimes known, consists of three radar transmitters and six receivers located in a line stretching across the southern United States from California to Georgia. It is known as a fence because the NAVSPASUR is in essence a 24,000-km high fence of radar energy, through which all satellites with inclinations of 33 degrees or more must pass twice a day. As a spacecraft passes through the fence the reflected radar energy is received by the six receivers and the satellite's position can be accurately fixed. The fence has given excellent service since it was built in 1961 and it could, on its own, maintain around 75 per cent of the US space surveillance catalogue, without the help of any other radar sensors. The fence headquarters is in Dahlgren, Virginia.

The Soviet Union publishes almost nothing about its military space effort. However we do know that it has a BMEWS system quite similar to the US system and

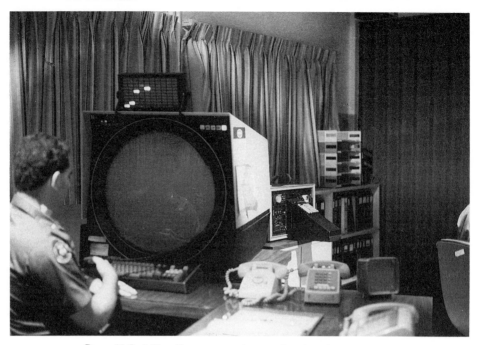

PLATE 11.5. A Pave Paws operator's control station. (*USAF Photo*)

PLATE 11.6. An operator's control station at the Space Surveillance Center HQ in NORAD's Cheyenne Mountain Complex. (*USAF Photo*)

PLATE 11.7. The Soviet Union's space tracking facility at Dushanbe in the Soviet Union.
(*US DoD Photo*)

that it has satellite tracking facilities worldwide, in friendly nations. The Soviets also have a fleet of impressive satellite support vessels, which can be deployed to optimum locations to support space missions.

Using radar, it is difficult to track satellites which have highly eccentric, geo-

PLATE 11.8. The Soviet Union's space support ship *Marshal Nedelin*. (*US DoD Photo*)

synchronous or other kinds of high altitude orbits. In fact, many of these satellites are beyond the range of the radar trackers, so optical tracking systems are used. Optical tracking, in summary, relies on recording the passage of a faint sunlit satellite across a fixed star field. The first system to be used by the United States was the Baker-Nunn camera which entered service as early as 1957. The camera's 20-inch optics can record objects as faint as the fourteenth magnitude and were first used to photograph Sputnik-1. Baker-Nunn cameras are now being phased out by the United States, but they are still used to photograph satellites at geosynchronous height. The last two remaining US systems are at San Vito in Italy and St Margarets in New Brunswick, Canada.

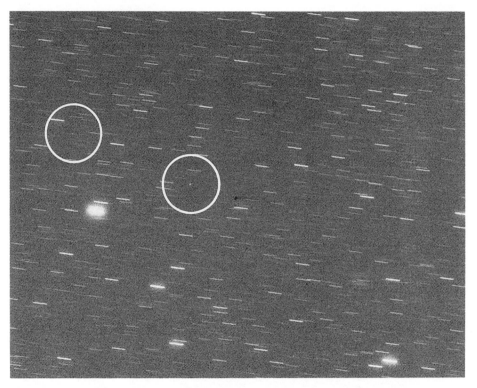

PLATE 11.9. Image from a Baker-Nunn camera. Long exposure time causes the stars to appear as short streaks, while the geostationary satellites appear as dots of light (circled). (*Canadian Forces, SITU, St Margarets*)

Satellite Identification

The detection and tracking of objects in space is also the first step in the next procedure for consideration: identification of the object. Often the orbital parameters give a strong indication of the role of the craft. For instance a craft in Sun-synchronous orbit will probably have optical sensors. Also patterns of operation have built up with time and the orbital parameters can quickly help confirm a new craft's place in such a pattern.

Despite this initial hint from the orbit details, the only way to identify a craft is to have a really good look at it. Remember that as a satellite goes into orbit, it takes with it several pieces of booster, shrouds, etc. Each piece might have to be checked in some detail to see if more than one satellite went into orbit. One way that satellites are different from orbiting junk is that the junk tends to tumble whereas the satellite will maintain a stabilised orientation in space.

Optical signatures of satellites and junk are therefore quite different. Similar techniques using radar could also be used, looking for a 'glint' on the return signals as an indication of tumbling. Infra-red techniques could also help identification because a satellite with power on will radiate heat, whereas a dead satellite or a piece of junk will be almost as cold as space itself.

The GEODSS (Ground-based Electro Optical Deep Space Surveillance) system is the device used by the United States to assist in the identification of objects in deep space using optical light. GEODSS can be thought of as the generation following Baker-Nunn camera technology. It is an electro-optical system and therefore relies not on film but on TV-type technology. The United States has an operational network of GEODSS electro-optical observatories around the Earth at New Mexico,

PLATE 11.10. One of the US Air Force's Ground-based Electro-Optical Deep Space Surveillance System (GEODSS) sites. (*TRW Photo*)

South Korea, Hawaii, Diego Garcia, and a further site in Portugal is planned for completion in 1989. Once complete, these five sites will provide full coverage of the geosynchronous satellite belt.

At each GEODSS site, two one-metre instruments are used, along with a 40-cm auxilliary. The auxilliary is a 76-cm focal length camera, providing a wide, six-degree field of view for routine observations, whereas the main one-metre instruments have focal lengths of 218 cm and a much narrower, 2.1-degree field of view. The GEODSS main instruments can track targets as faint as magnitude 16 or 'a football at geo-stationary height (36,000 km)'. Once the GEODSS has detected a possible satellite, a 12x zoom capability is used to make a detailed evaluation of the craft's motion. Clearly, at these great distances one would not be able to obtain a clear image of satellite shape, but the system can discriminate between a stable satellite and a tumbling piece of orbital debris.

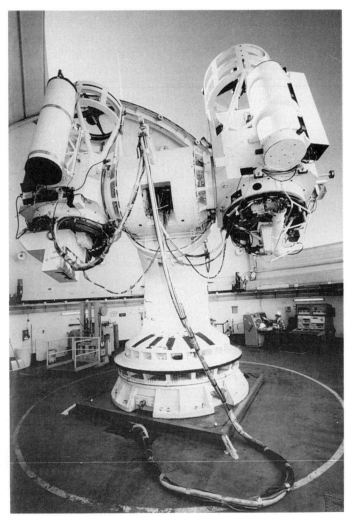

PLATE 11.11. The dual 1.2-metre telescopes of the US Maui Optical Tracking and Identification Facility (MOTIF) facility based in Maui, Hawaii. (*USAF Photo*)

A powerful system within the US tracking network is the MOTIF (Maui Optical Tracking and Identification Facility) at Mount Haleakala, Maui, which is co-located with the Hawaiian GEODSS. MOTIF has two 1.2-metre telescopes that are controlled on a single mount. The two telescopes not only look in the visible wavelengths but also in the infra-red. The variety of detectors allow multispectral data, direct images and positional data to be gathered from satellites at all altitudes. The MOTIF low-light-level TV can detect objects as faint as magnitude 19.

The most powerful telescope at Maui, used for space identification, is the AMOS (Air Force Maui Optical Station) 1.6-metre telescope. Individual parts of a satellite can be identified using this system. Plate 11.12 shows an image of the US Skylab satellite, on which the main body and solar panels are easily recognisable.

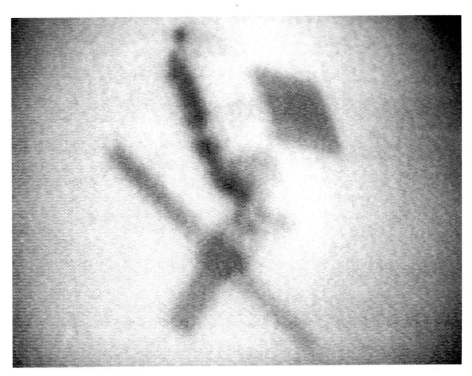

PLATE 11.12. This photograph of Skylab was obtained using the Air Force Maui Optical Station 1.6 metre telescope operated by Avco Research Laboratory. (*TEXTRON*)

Space Catalogue

Hundreds of objects are launched into orbit each year and also many objects decay from orbit during the same period. However, in net terms, the total number of large (bigger than a baseball) objects in orbit is continuing to rise and currently exceeds 7,000. The orbits of those 7,000-plus objects are all affected by the gravitation perturbations described in Chapter 2 and so change continuously. Keeping tabs on all these objects is therefore a continuous and complex task. The first step to formalising this task is the creation of a catalogue, or database, of the objects in orbit and details of their orbital parameters.

Not only must the space surveillance systems of both the United States and Soviet

Union maintain such databases for military purposes but, equally, any agency interested in space operations must also have such a database, or at least access to one. For example, NASA and the UK's Royal Aircraft Establishment at Farnborough both maintain and publish their own lists of orbiting objects, together with their orbital details. To get over the problem of differing serial number systems, an international designator is assigned to each object tracked. The designator indicates the year of launch, the launch number within the year and the object type. For example, 1987–95A was the ninety-fifth launch in 1987. The suffix A indicates that this object was the payload; in fact it was the West German satellite TV-Sat 1. Successive suffixes (eg, 1987–95B) indicate launcher bodies or launch debris.

Maintaining and Using the Space Database

The surveillance tasks already covered have an end product: the database of all known man-made objects in space. To be of any real use, this data base must be kept current and any change or new feature must be added as quickly as possible. This need for urgency is clear if one considers the database as the routine space traffic 'picture' against which any new event will stand out and trigger an alert. Space tracking resources must therefore continuously refine the orbital parameters in the database by detecting and tracking each object as it comes into view. This task of continuous updating is very important because some extra objects can appear in orbit without any launch detection. Also, working satellites may have their orbits adjusted from time to time. To further complicate the issue, old satellites and launcher bodies sometimes explode without any warning, scattering perhaps hundreds of pieces into space. The space tracking network must then meticulously track and log those individual pieces which are large enough to be detected. Surprisingly, around half the objects being tracked have resulted from such break-ups. Old satellites and launchers still containing traces of hypergolic propellants are the main culprits. Either pressures build up over time or the propellants mix somehow and an explosion occurs. The US Delta LV's second stage caused just such problems, and between 1973 and 1981 seven of these explosions resulted in 1,200 extra pieces in the catalogue. The problem was solved in 1981 by programming the Deltas to burn all their propellants so that nothing remained.

Military activity has also caused problems because of planned satellite destruction. For example, both the Americans and the Soviets have tested their ASAT weapons in space and caused thousands of pieces of orbiting debris of both the targets and the ASATs. Many of these pieces are too small to be tracked from Earth. Despite good explanations for many spacecraft explosions, around half of those craft which break up in orbit do so for no apparent reason.

Because of the danger of collision with one of the thousands of orbiting objects, prior to any space launch, programmes are run to check for possible orbital conflictions. The fact that perhaps no conflicts are computed is no reason to relax because there are still a further estimated 40,000 objects in orbit, smaller than a baseball but larger than a pea, and nobody knows where they are! Not only that, but each is moving at around 7 km/sec and so has the destructive power of a cannonball. The picture becomes even gloomier if one were to worry about the countless thousands of very small pieces, each also a potential satellite killer. This orbiting junkyard is the legacy of civil and military space programmes and a wanton disregard of the growing problem. The probability of a satellite being hit and damaged is now so high that structures have to be specially toughened to resist such an impact.

Knowledge of the orbital details of a satellite will allow space surveillance centres to estimate the time and place when and where the satellite will re-enter the Earth's atmosphere. Such estimation is far from being an exact science and is only accurate within 20 per cent of the time remaining in orbit. Typically, detailed decay predictions begin with around two weeks of orbital life remaining. Orbital details are then watched more closely than usual and possibly, for unusually shaped and large objects, identification systems will try to observe the orientation of the object. Orientation can have an effect once the craft is low enough to be subjected to aerodynamic forces. Around two hours prior to decay, final predictions will be made, accurate to about plus or minus 12 minutes. As a rule of thumb, objects with cross-sectional areas of one metre or greater will re-enter the atmosphere and strike the Earth; smaller objects will burn up due to the intense kinetic heating effects on re-entry.

One reason for keeping close watch on re-entering objects is to give advance warning to those countries on which the object might fall. Equally, because the re-entering object will exhibit many of the qualities of a re-entering ICBM, great precautions are necessary to ensure that its identity is not mistaken.

THE FUTURE

Extrapolation of current data indicates that by the year 2000 the number of objects tracked will increase to around 10,000. Space surveillance seems therefore to be a growth business for some time to come.

We have currently entered the second generation of space surveillance sensors, such as Pave Paws and GEODSS. No doubt the next generation will arrive in the early 2000s, perhaps with a greater emphasis on space-based sensors, such as the BSTS (Boost Surveillance Tracking Satellite) planned to replace the DSP series of launch warning satellites. Also, spacecraft identification is currently very crude and slow to yield detailed data. This area could also benefit from research and development effort, particularly in the field of space-based optical sensors.

In the meantime, however, the surveillance of space continues to benefit both military and civilian space agencies alike. On the one hand it helps the military with ICBM warning and contributes towards space control, and on the other, because of the congestion of Earth orbits, it provides the space traffic control function which allows civil launch agencies to achieve orbit more safely.

12

Space Warfare

The militarisation of space can be considered to have stemmed from the development of ICBMs in the 1950s. These missiles can reach altitudes in excess of 1,000 km and therefore exit the atmosphere and travel through space for part of their flight-paths. There have been a number of attempts over the years to limit, and even reduce, the numbers of these strategic ballistic missiles and there are now encouraging discussions between the two Superpowers. However, the motives for reducing the number of ICBMs are more fundamental than the fact that they would pass through space. Instead, most of the debate on militarisation has concentrated on the three areas of the military roles of satellites, the threat of attack on satellites and, more recently, on possible breaches of the ABM Treaty with the consequent implications for international stability. This chapter will concentrate on the physical threat to objects in space with particular reference to satellites and ballistic missiles.

ANTI-SATELLITE WEAPONS

Following the launch of Sputnik by the Soviets in 1957, both Superpowers recognised the value of satellites and the potential threat posed to national security by the other's craft. Consequently, both sides started to develop ASAT weapons. On first inspection, satellites make splendid targets for they are thin-skinned vehicles packed with delicate equipment. Their power is derived from large, sensitive solar arrays and, as they rely on optical devices for maintaining their orientation, they are vulnerable to 'blinding'. Moreover, once established in orbit they tend to fly on predictable tracks against a clear space background, making them readily discernible. It has not yet been thought necessary to provide them with self-defence armament but measures are being taken to raise their resistance to nuclear radiation and to reduce their susceptibility to laser attack. On the other hand, orbital targets are at least 200 km from the Earth's surface, are moving at about 8 km/sec at that altitude and, at perhaps only 10 metres across, are quite small.

If an attack on a satellite is contemplated there are two fundamental techniques. In the first the interceptor can be launched from any point on Earth provided it is within range and it approaches its target in a direct ascent. With this method the anti-satellite interceptor, or ASAT, is at high speed and the total time for the interception is in the order of 10 minutes. In order to be successful the ASAT requires either a very accurate homing head and considerable computational and tracking resources or a very large (possibly nuclear) warhead to compensate for terminal homing inaccuracies. The second method is known as the co-planar interception and demands that the ASAT be launched into the same plane as its target. This in turn means that the interceptor must be launched when its site is directly beneath the orbital plane of the target, an event that occurs only twice per day. This second method is more forgiving in that if the target has already overflown when the launch site revolves into plane, it is possible to launch into a lower (and therefore faster) trajectory and effect an interception. If, however, the target has not overflown when the launch site comes into plane the ASAT can be launched into a higher (and thus slower) orbit until the target catches up and the ASAT can descend for the kill. Adjustment of the ASAT's position around its orbit to carry out the interception is not difficult provided there is sufficient time available. In practice, though, the intercept must be completed within two orbits of the ASAT otherwise the satellite operator can detect the attacker and has time to manoeuvre his victim out of harm's way.

Initially, the United States considered ground-, submarine- and air-launched concepts for ASATs and by 1964 had installed missiles on Kwajalein Island in the Pacific Ocean. These Nike-Zeus missiles and their Thor successors were armed with nuclear warheads in recognition of the inaccuracy of missile guidance in those days. A major disadvantage of the large radius of effect was demonstrated during a series of high altitude nuclear weapon tests in 1962. One of the detonations in the Starfish series disabled a number of satellites with its gamma and X-ray radiations and thus became the first, though unintentional, ASAT weapon. One test also had its effect on ground equipment when power and telephone links in the Hawaiian Islands were interrupted for several days even though that test was several hundred kilometres from overhead those Islands. The Limited Test Ban Treaty of 1963 brought an end to these nuclear tests in space. Even though that treaty does not rule out possession of ASATs with nuclear warheads, it seems that the United States is mindful of the distinct possibility of an own goal against its electronic equipments and now has abandoned them for such applications. Nevertheless, the United States maintained its ASATs in the Pacific area until 1975 but since then has had no deployed ASAT capability.

The Soviet Union began its ASAT effort in 1967 and deployed the operational system based on the SS-9 ICBM in 1971. Up to 1982 it had conducted 20 tests of which nine are reported to have been successful using the co-planar method of interception. All the targets were launched from Plesetsk while the ASATs were fired from Tyuratam and all the reportedly successful interceptions were conducted within two orbits. The ASAT is said to be fitted with a large fragmentation warhead giving it an effective radius of about a kilometre. It is also assessed that the earlier, and successful, tests employed radar homing while the later tests used infra-red sensing which requires further development. It is perhaps significant that with apparently only moderate success and with the last test conducted in 1982, the Soviets may be looking at an entirely different approach to ASAT weapons.

The shortcomings of the Soviets' favoured co-planar method of ASAT interception are largely overcome with the latest development from the United States. Persevering with the direct ascent technique, it has tested an MHV (Miniature Homing Vehicle) built by Vought. The MHV weighs only 16 kg and measures about 33 by 30 cm. It seeks its target by means of eight infra-red telescopes. As these sensors must stare at the target throughout the interception lateral manoeuvres are made

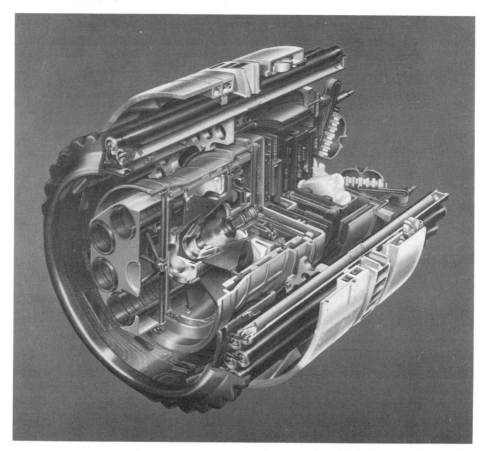

PLATE 12.1. Anti-satellite miniature homing vehicle. (*USAF*)

possible by 56 single-shot solid rockets placed longitudinally around the circumference of the vehicle. It has no moving parts and is spun about its longitudinal axis to provide stability while a ring laser gyro linked with an advanced microcomputer is at the heart of the guidance system. Unlike the Soviet ASAT weapon, the MHV has no warhead but relies on its accurate homing and guidance to ensure destruction of its target by collision at high velocity. In other words, it is a KKW (Kinetic Kill Weapon)—a term used extensively in connection with the research of weapon systems for space and ballistic missile defences.

The great advance in this direct ascent method of interception, with the MHV incorporated into a 5.2-metre long missile weighing 1,200 kg, derives from the use of an F-15 Eagle aircraft as a launch vehicle. A 'celestial' Eagle could be deployed widely over the Earth's surface to bring it within range of its target. In this manner the United States could be freed from the infrequent launch opportunities available to a ground-based system. In the first instance the aircraft receives its target details while still on the ground. Thereafter, the aircraft systems generate commands which are displayed on the pilot's head-up display in the cockpit. Typically, the aircraft would climb to a height of about 40,000 feet at near sonic speed before entering a steep climb for the missile launch. The weapon would then climb under inertial guidance until at orbital altitude the MHV would be detached and continue under its own guidance to impact.

PLATE 12.2. Launch of an anti-satellite missile from an F-15 aircraft on 27 September 1985.
(*US DoD Photo*)

The MHV has been tested five times. Following four test firings into space to prove the sensors and guidance, the fifth test was against a satellite which was decisively dispatched. This development looked promising and it was planned to conduct 12 tests before deploying two F-15 squadrons to the east and west coasts of the country. However, in December 1985 Congress banned any further tests of the device against targets in space. It seems that they were concerned that such testing might prove an obstacle to progress on arms control talks with the Soviet Union. No doubt that ban could have been quickly relaxed if the latter was to restart its testing but, because of budget constraints in early 1988, the programme was cancelled.

A logical progression for ASAT weapons is the employment of ground-based beams or DEW (Direct Energy Weapons)—the death rays of science fiction. DEWs have an advantage over missiles in that the speed of delivery of their destructive energy is considerably faster than that for missiles, in effect giving a zero 'time of flight'. Thus the tracking and pointing problems associated with a fast-moving target could be greatly simplified. It is assumed that low-orbiting satellites, probably conducting a form of surveillance, would be regarded as the most threatening and be the first in line for disablement or destruction. At heights of 200 to 800 km, these satellites would be moving at 7 to 8 km/sec and therefore offer only a short period on each orbit for attack by any ground-based weapon. As an example, a satellite orbiting at 200 km directly over the site would be above the horizon for about seven minutes and, to take full advantage of those seven minutes, a weapon range of 1,500 km would be needed. Any displacement of the orbit from the overhead would reduce that time. At a higher orbital altitude a satellite is visible longer and a weapon's maximum range becomes an increasingly important factor. However, since successive satellite ground tracks are displaced and there would be few opportunities for attack by any single ground-based weapon, a number of defensive sites would be needed to quickly destroy a particular satellite. If the reports of ASAT facilities in the Soviet Union are to be believed, it would appear that nation has a network of complementary techniques to provide multiple daily engagements of all low Earth

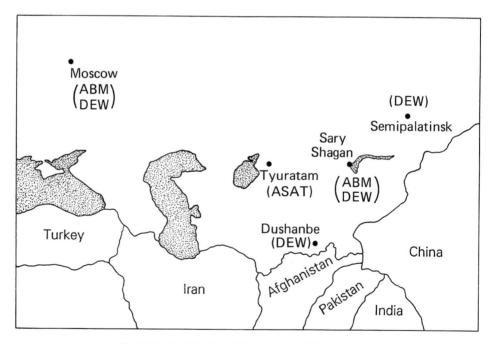

FIG 12.1. Possible sites of Soviet anti-satellite weapons.

orbiting satellites (Figure 12.1) A further development of the use of ASAT weapons might be their deployment in space but if there are any such plans they have not been made public by East or West. The types of weapons that might be used for this purpose might be adaptations of those described later in this chapter for ABM purposes.

BALLISTIC MISSILE DEFENCE

It might be imagined that the task of attacking an ICBM, or one of its warheads, is similar to that of taking on a satellite. However, while there is some similarity in part of their trajectories (Figure 12.2) they are fundamentally different targets both in their construction and in the threat which they pose. The methods of ASAT attack have already been described and to date these are not constrained by treaty. By contrast the format of BMD (Ballistic Missile Defence) is prescribed by the ABM Treaty. It is perhaps predictable, therefore, that the developments by the United States and Soviet Union in the field of BMD have been remarkably similar. Both sides have produced ground-based high-acceleration missiles armed with nuclear warheads designed to destroy incoming ballistic missile warheads in the later stages of their trajectory. Thus the Spartan and Sprint missiles deployed by the United States in the 1970s are directly comparable to the Soviet Galosh and Gazelle missiles. The difference is that the United States decommissioned its missiles in 1976 and has not replaced them, while the Soviet Union retains its two types. So although there is a common approach in employing missiles for both ASAT and BMD purposes, other modes of attack would have to be used to extend the vulnerability of the warhead beyond its terminal descent to the target.

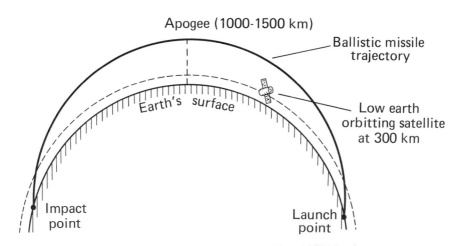

FIG 12.2. Comparison of satellite low Earth orbit and ICBM trajectory.

The whole concept of defence against ballistic missiles was placed under the microscope following President Reagan's SDI speech on 23 March 1983:

> What if free people could live secure in the knowledge that their security did not rest upon the threat of instant US retaliation to deter a Soviet attack, that we would intercept and destroy strategic ballistic missiles before they reached our own soil or that of our allies?

In that speech he was, in effect, challenging the United States technology base to do the necessary research to find a means to 'free the world from the threat of nuclear war'. The Initiative appeared to be a profound moral stance against deterrence of aggression through the promise of retaliation. It may, though, have had a more practical foundation—a recognition of the developments in Soviet offences and defences. Accuracy of their ICBMs was being improved so that they were approaching a disabling capability against the United States land-based strategic systems. Those ICBMs themselves were also becoming less vulnerable by virtue of extensive silo-hardening programmes and by the imminent introduction of mobile (SS-24 and SS-25) missiles, both innovations which would complicate US retaliation plans. The development of SAM (Surface to Air Missiles) for air defence which could also engage ICBMs further threatened those plans. Furthermore, if the reports of extensive laser and particle-beam research which could have applications to advanced weapons were true, the Soviets might achieve a technological 'break-out' and place the United States at a strategic disadvantage. Regardless of the reasons behind it, the Initiative frames a formidable technical task and has set in train research into a very wide field of technology. Out of that speech has grown an extensive examination of the feasibility of providing a layered defensive system to defeat ballistic missiles at any point of their trajectories.

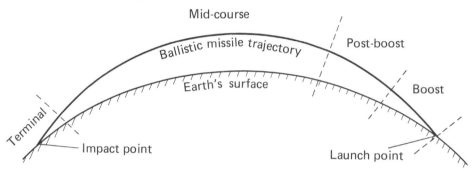

FIG 12.3. Ballistic missile phases.

BALLISTIC MISSILE TRAJECTORIES

In deciding how best to defend against ICBMs it is useful to analyse their flight-paths. An ICBM path can be sub-divided into four distinct phases, namely boost, post-boost, mid-course and terminal. In the former there is a massive expenditure of chemical energy which is translated into a rocket velocity that in turn yields the required range of its warhead. When the fuel is spent the booster separates after typically three to five minutes and re-enters the atmosphere to be consumed in a fiery re-entry while the warhead bus continues on its sinister path. In the post-boost phase the very large infra-red plume which is associated with the boost phase has ended and only a small amount of propulsion is needed to place each of up to 10 warheads on very precise trajectories for their individual targets. This process consumes five to eight minutes during which time decoys and chaff, known as penetration aids, also will be dispensed. In this period the bus carrying the warheads and decoys will be navigated very accurately by inertial means. The following mid-course phase is the longest and may last 15 to 25 minutes depending on range to target. The threat cloud of warheads and penetration aids all travel through space without any vestige of propulsion or evasive actions. In the fourth and final phase the RVs (Re-entry Vehicles), or warheads, penetrate the atmosphere from about 100 km altitude to their targets. The RVs are at high speed and this phase lasts only about one minute.

In analysing the overall trajectory, a number of distinctive features can be associated with each of the four phases. An ICBM can be easily detected and tracked from space by virtue of its very hot rocket efflux in the boost phase. The booster is a 'softer' target than the denser and more robust warheads and a successful attack in this first phase could nullify multiple warheads. However, this phase is the most distant from the defender, so space resources for detection, surveillance and attack may be needed. In the post-boost phase the warhead bus is less easily detected without a large rocket plume and the cooler body necessitates different sensors. The earlier a successful attack can be made in this phase the greater the return in terms of warheads killed and the number of decoys that can be prevented from deploying. A complicating factor for defences in the following mid-course phase is the potentially large number of penetration aids which could accompany the warheads. Regardless of their relative weights, shapes and sizes, all these objects would travel through the near-vacuum of space at the same velocity. This gives the defender the task of attacking every object unless he can distinguish the threatening warheads from the distracting but unimportant penetration aids. Any confusion caused by the penetration aids is removed during the re-entry phase for they would be destroyed by kinetic heating as they returned to the denser atmosphere. The warheads are protected from a similar fate by an ablative coating which evaporates as the temperature rises and in so doing protects the warheads themselves. The element of confusion may have been removed in this phase but there is precious little time for the defender to react. Thus it can be concluded that the most advantageous phase for the defender to attack an ICBM is in the boost phase. Additionally, if he is to avoid the expense of attacking worthless objects in the mid-course phase and guard against saturation of his terminal defences through insufficient earlier success, he must develop a means of discriminating between warheads and penetration aids.

WEAPON TYPES

The SDI has brought about a remarkable disclosure of the means by which strategic defences might enhance US national security. This is unusual as concepts and research for such sensitive matters normally remain highly classified and are pursued behind dense veils of secrecy. It is this openness on the part of the United States which allows an early discussion of the methods which might be adopted if enhanced strategic defences are to be deployed in the future. Lest it be thought that the SDI is solely a Western pursuit, it is worth recalling the words of Mr Gorbachev, General Secretary of the Communist Part of the Soviet Union, in a TV interview on 30 November 1987. In discussing the SDI he said:

> Generally, it's difficult to say what the Soviet Union is not doing. It is doing virtually everything that the USA is doing. Very likely we are engaged in research, basic research, which relates to those aspects which are covered by SDI in the USA.

Thus, in describing Western deliberations and research projects on strategic defence, the Eastern efforts are probably also being covered.

CHEMICAL ROCKETS

The most mature of all weapon technologies for ABM purposes is that of chemical rockets which can draw on years of development. The essential principles remain identical but in earlier days the missile control and guidance were less precise and needed a very large warhead, usually nuclear, with the radius of effect to take account of the overall system inaccuracy. However, as demonstrated by high-altitude nuclear weapon tests, they can have a disastrous effect on communications, radar and other unprotected electronic equipment and, in that sense, could act against the interests of the defender. With these difficulties, and because guidance technology has advanced apace to render nuclear warheads unnecessary, the United States appears to have turned its back on such devices. The maturity of this form of defence could allow the United States to deploy a final layer of ABM missiles by the mid-1990s if it so wished. The provisions of the ABM Treaty (Chapter 4), however, would set a limit of 100 missiles which could provide only a partial counter to the thousands of Soviet warheads. Nevertheless, the United States has tested its FLAG (Flexible Lightweight Agile Guided) missile in the development of a high-speed missile with advanced guidance that is capable of neutralising its target by collision, ie as a KKW. In this way no warhead would be needed. Homing would be by means of infra-red sensing by detecting and tracking the incoming target which is 'hotter' than its space background. This is no easy task, for the temperature differences between the body and background are small and the high kinetic heating of the hypersonic interceptor missile's nosecone demands cooling to aid its sensor's discrimination. Difficult as it may be, two developmental FLAG missiles have demonstrated successful interceptions of their high-speed targets. The principle of infra-red homing of chemically powered rockets had already been demonstrated with the HOE (Homing Overlay Experiment) in 1984. A Minuteman ICBM was intercepted by collision and without a warhead over intercontinental distance by another Minuteman (Plate 12.3). The FLAG missile firings are technology demonstrations for two other missile concepts known as HEDI (High Endoatmospheric Defence Interceptor) and the longer-range ERIS (Exoatmospheric Re-entry Interceptor Subsystem). Both HEDI and ERIS, designed for interception within and outside the atmosphere, respectively, are set for demonstration firings in the early 1990s. Chemical rockets have maturity of development on their side and have the potential of timeliness in their operational deployment, but they are limited in their range and speed of intercept, so other technologies are being researched to possibly augment or replace them in the defensive inventory.

ELECTROMAGNETIC RAILGUN

One field of research makes use of the electromagnetic acceleration of projectiles to very high velocities with a development known as an EMR (Electromagnetic Railgun). The EMR (Figure 12.4) has two parallel rails with a projectile placed between them. A current source swiftly applied to the rails it passes along one rail, through a conducting armature behind the projectile, and returns along the other rail. The resultant magnetic field F, reinforced with that from the armature, accelerates the projectile between the rails and down the gun 'barrel'. Projectile

PLATE 12.3. Launch of a Homing Overlay Experimental interceptor missile which successfully intercepted an incoming re-entry vehicle by collision. (*US DoD Photo*)

speeds in excess of 10 km/sec have been achieved which compare with a rifle bullet
at perhaps one-tenth of that velocity. Although the projectiles may be only a few

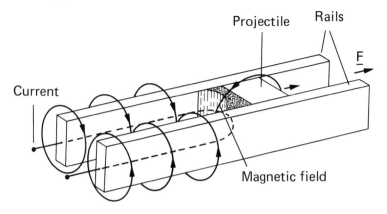

FIG 12.4. Electromagnetic railgun schematic.

grams they possess great destructive capability with their high kinetic energy. Plate 12.4 shows the damage inflicted on a cast aluminium block by a seven-gram projectile fired at 7 km/sec. Much development is still needed to produce rails capable of withstanding rapid rates of fire and to provide the very high power-generation and power-storage devices. To fire several 0.5–1 kg projectiles in a second at velocities in excess of 10 km/sec would require millions of kilowatts of power with currents of the order of a million amps. The challenge of providing power of this magnitude on Earth is magnified severalfold if these potential weapons are to be deployed to space.

LASERS

Energy is released when electrons, ions or molecules that have been excited revert to a lower energy level. The frequency of this radiated energy is dependent on the material used and the method of excitation. A laser (Light Amplification by Stimulated Emission of Radiation) is a device which uses this principle to produce a highly monochromatic (single wavelength) and coherent beam (all waves in phase). The intensity of incoherent radiation is limited by the temperature of the material producing the radiation but laser radiation has no such limit and, when its beam is sufficiently bright, it can damage by heat or shock action. Radiation may be in the infra-red, visible, ultra violet or X-ray parts of the electromagnetic spectrum and four types of laser are known to be under research for possible use as weapons.

Chemical Lasers

The most mature of the laser types is the chemical laser in which two atomic gases are introduced into a combustion chamber. They may react spontaneously or be excited by an electrical discharge and their atoms are excited to higher energy levels. As the atoms revert to former energy levels they emit their characteristic wavelength. The reflective inner surface of the laser tube reflects these light waves which combine to produce the coherent laser beam through a semi-transparent mirror at one end of the laser (Figure 12.5). Elements and compounds lase at

PLATE 12.4. Damage to an aluminium block caused by an electromagnetic railgun.
(*US DoD Photo*)

characteristic wavelengths, thus a CO_2 (carbon dioxide) laser lases at 10.7 microns (millionths of a metre) while an HF (Hydrogen Fluoride) laser employing a combination of hydrogen and fluorine lases at a wavelength of 2.7 microns. Following normal electromagnetic principles, the shorter the wavelength the smaller the focusing mirror or antenna that is needed. Thus the cross-sectional area of a HF laser can be less than that of a CO_2 laser. Additionally, the HF laser's higher frequency means that it has greater efficiency and therefore destructive power when its energy impinges on a target. The highest-powered HF laser known to the public is the US Navy's MIRACL (Mid Infra-Red Advanced Chemical Laser) rated at 2.2 megawatts.

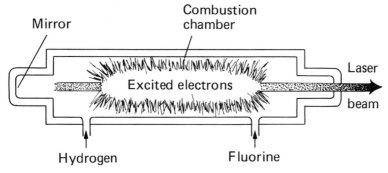

FIG 12.5. Hydrogen fluoride laser schematic.

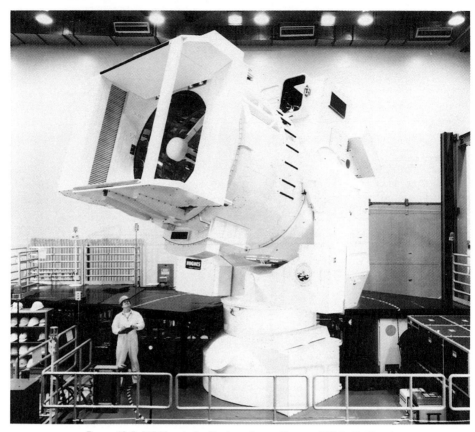

PLATE 12.5. US Navy's Sealite laser beam director (*US DoD Photo*)

This laser was linked with the Navy's own Sealite beam director (Plate 12.5) in a static test against a Titan missile in 1986. The missile was pressurised to simulate flight loads and was destroyed (Plate 12.6). This provides an indication of the vulnerability of missiles in the boost phase but several orders of additional brightness will be required from a laser in order to destroy the much tougher warheads. Another consideration in selecting a laser by its wavelength is its transmission characteristic. The atmosphere effectively blocks most laser wavelengths but there are certain narrow windows. For instance, wavelengths of between 0.3 and 1 micron are effectively transmitted and there are other such 'conduits'. The characteristic wavelength of the CO_2 laser is apparently readily transmitted but it has high attenuation in the presence of water vapour and would be limited by weather in many ground-based applications. Furthermore, lasers at longer wavelengths suffer from greater beam divergence. In summary, lasers with shorter wavelengths are the most promising because of their greater potential destructiveness and, as they promise to be more compact, they offer the possibility of being deployed in space.

Excimer Laser

An excimer (or excited dimer) laser employs two atomic gases, typically a noble gas (eg, argon, krypton or xenon) and a halogen (eg, chlorine or fluorine). When

PLATE 12.6. Destruction of a Titan missile by laser (*US DoD Photo*)

ionised by the passage of a pulsed electron beam, pulses of laser radiation are produced. A characteristic of excimer lasers is a shorter wavelength, typically 0.3 to 0.5 micron, than chemical lasers. This permits a less bulky and less heavy laser although the required high electrical power delivered in short pulses is likely to remain a major challenge. Much development is still needed with this type of laser which promises a higher efficiency than a chemical laser, but a high weight-to-power output may mean it would be more suitable for ground deployment.

Free Electron Laser

Charged particles emit radiation when under the influence of a magnetic field. This principle is exploited in an FEL (Free Electron Laser) to provide laser radiation. A beam of high energy electrons is passed through alternating magnetic fields to pro-

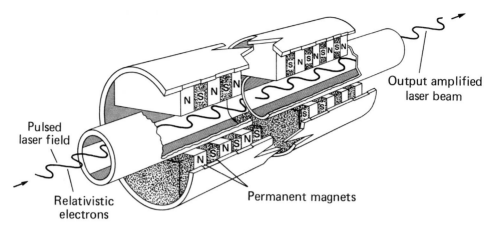

Pulsed
laser field

Output amplified
laser beam

Relativistic
electrons

Permanent magnets

FIG 12.6. Free electron laser schematic.

duce coherent laser radiation (Figure 12.6). The wavelength of that laser beam is dependent on the periodicity of the magnetic field and on the electron energy and thus, by varying one or both of these parameters, the resultant wavelength can be varied. This type of laser promises higher energy efficiency than other lasers, perhaps of the order of 40 per cent and, by tuning the wavelength between 0.1 and 20 microns to penetrate the atmosphere, the laser can be ground-based. This is useful as the greatest disadvantage of an FEL is its need for a large accelerator, and thus power source, to generate the electron beam.

X-Ray Laser

The concept with potentially the greatest power as a weapon is the X-ray laser. In this device the 'pumping' of the lasing material would be achieved by a small nuclear explosion and the resultant destructive X-rays would be transmitted along numerous lasing rods towards their targets in the fraction of a second before the laser itself is vaporised. The very short wavelengths of the radiation would dictate that both the laser and its targets would have to be in space as the beam would be quickly absorbed by the atmosphere. Permanent basing of these lasers in space would contravene the Outer Space Treaty, so perhaps a concept of launch just before their use might be considered.

PARTICLE BEAM WEAPONS

The electromagnetic beams of lasers consist of pure energy. This contrasts with beams of sub-atomic particles (eg, protons, electrons, ions or neutral atoms) in which the particles are accelerated by electromagnetic fields to very high velocities. Beams of this latter type have been used for a number of years in research into high energy physics. For particle beams to be used as weapons their energy would have to be focused into a narrow beam of very high intensity. It is necessary to use charged particles in order to accelerate them by electromagnetic means but these particles would be mutually repelled within the beam and be deflected by the Earth's magnetic field and so would be difficult to aim. Therefore a neutral beam would be preferable. By stripping off the negative charge from a charged beam by means of an 'ion stripper', a neutral beam travelling in excess of half the speed of light can be generated, but it remains to be seen whether such a beam can be harnessed to act as a weapon. Even in the rarer levels of the atmosphere electrons would be stripped from a neutral beam to produce a charged beam. Therefore a neutral particle beam weapon would have to be based in space (above 100 km) and be employed against space targets. However, the considerable weight of the electron generator would present a formidable obstacle to space basing.

A neutral particle beam could penetrate deep into most materials and damage them by altering their molecular structure. Moreover, the beam would be highly destructive to electronic circuits and would need less delivered energy than lasers. This particle beam advantage would be considerably diminished, however, if the electronic circuits of the target are hardened against ionising radiation (nuclear hardened).

WEAPON APPLICATIONS

From the description of the weapon technologies it is apparent that they can be divided into two separate categories: ground- and space-based. KKWs and lasers could be in either category, but X-ray lasers and particle beam weapons must be deployed into space to be effective. The basing of these potential weapons in turn defines the part of a ballistic missile trajectory against which they might be used. Ground-based KKWs could be used to attack incoming warheads in their terminal and late mid-course phases, while space-based KKWs might be capable of attacking ballistic missiles earlier, even in the boost phase, providing a great advantage to the defending side. While ground-based lasers could also be used in the latter part of the trajectory their effective range could be markedly increased by reflecting their energy from space-based mirrors onwards to their targets. Alternatively, lasers could be placed in space where, if the laser wavelengths can penetrate the atmosphere, potentially they could attack ballistic missiles or their warheads over their complete flightpath.

The number of laser, particle beam weapon or KKW satellites required in a constellation to provide a high probability of destroying a given number of attacking warheads depends on a number of factors. The higher the orbiting weapons the greater their theoretical cover of launch sites, but an increase in height is only helpful if those weapons have the range to exploit their increased field of view. Another consideration is the retargeting time after the destruction of a target; more rapid retargeting would permit a smaller constellation. The constellation size would also be governed by the number of KKWs on a given satellite and, in the case of a laser or particle beam weapons, on the 'brightness' of the weapon. A brighter or more powerful weapon would deal with its target in a shorter time and allow quicker retargeting, but target 'hardness' would also be a factor. From the orbital descriptions in Chapter 2 it will be clear that the non-repetitive nature of each satellite's track means that several hundred weapon satellites could be needed to give a con-

PLATE 12.7. Artist's impression of a space-based mirror reflecting laser energy towards a target. (*US DoD*)

tinuous capability. Moreover, the greater the constellation's desired effectiveness, the greater the number of defensive satellites needed. Finally, the geographic distribution of the enemy's launch sites would be influential.

Paradoxically, a greater geographical spread of sites could reduce the demands on a defensive constellation with more satellites able to view sites or missiles at any time. This could also reduce the risk of saturation of defences that might occur with denser basing.

SURVEILLANCE

To bring ABM weapons to bear requires a high order of detection and surveillance of the missiles. Launch detection satellites at synchronous altitudes already maintain watch for launches from large areas of the Earth's surface and these systems may suffice to provide the early warning and initial surveillance. However, after the boost phase, when the large infra-red signature of the booster rocket has died away, a different form of surveillance is needed. With considerably reduced infra-red energy associated with the post-boost phase, the target's temperature more closely resembles that of its background and the problem of surveillance is increased. Longer-wave infra-red sensors are needed and they must track every potentially offensive object, including opposing satellites which could be supporting the attack, to yield the necessary information to marshal an effective defence.

Additional surveillance can be provided by ground-based radar and optical means, the latter being subject to interference from cloud and precipitation. Space-based radar is a possibility but there are many difficulties, primarily heavy weight and high power requirements, to be overcome before this could supplant the more developed techniques of the ground versions. Infra-red sensors need not be space-based, and indeed the United States is developing a Boeing 767 aircraft, known as the AOA (Airborne Optical Adjunct), modified to carry long-wave infra-red sensors. This US Army project is to test the feasibility of tracking incoming objects in space and relaying the information to ground-based ABM systems for terminal defences. The AOA is scheduled to fly with its sensors in 1989 or 1990. For those warheads which

PLATE 12.8. The AOA Boeing 767 modified to carry infra-red sensors for space surveillance. (*US DoD Photo*)

have evaded the attentions of earlier weapons it is probable that the mature technology of ground-based radar would be used for detection and, as the warheads heat up with atmospheric friction, short-wave infra-red sensing could become a possibility.

DISCRIMINATION

It is not sufficient merely to survey the threat cloud of boosters, warheads and their associated penetration aids. There must be a process of discrimination between the threatening warheads and the unimportant objects to identify the targets and to avoid wasting weapons. Continuous high resolution surveillance may simplify the discrimination task by detecting, for instance, the inflation of decoy balloons. Alternatively, the objects might be precisely imaged by a laser radar (ladar) employing a low power visible or ultra-violet laser beam with the reflected light being detected by a telescope. Another research technique involves the use of a low power neutral particle beam to impinge on targets and measuring the form of the reradiated energy. Any hint of Gamma or X-ray radiation confirms the composition of the target as a warhead rather than decoy.

Yet another technique could employ a low-powered laser to strike the target while another high resolution sensor detects the target reaction. A light decoy would be deflected from its path more than a much heavier warhead and could form the basis of a discrimination technique. The high resolution sensors which might provide the required level of discrimination are almost certain to be 'active', ie, emanate energy to carry out their role. Thus they would themselves be susceptible to countermeasures. It might be advantageous, therefore, to employ a 'bistatic' system with a receiving sensor remote from the transmitter.

POINTING AND TRACKING

Having detected the targets it will be necessary to aim the weapons and continue to track the targets until they are neutralised. The challenges of pointing and tracking differ with the type of weapon. It may be sufficient to point KKWs towards their targets and allow in-built homing sensors to complete the task. For laser and particle beam weapons it would be necessary to track the target and point the weapon for a finite time to allow the energy to achieve the desired level of damage. An impression of the enormity of that task can be gauged by recognising that the target may be only a metre or two across and may be several thousands of kilometres away. Imagine tracking a dustbin-sized object moving at 20 times the speed of Concorde at a distance equal to the breadth of the United States. Formidable as that problem may appear, the NASA Space Telescope, already built and soon to be carried on a Shuttle flight for observation of deep space, has a pointing accuracy of 0.05 microradian or better than three-millionths of a degree. This approaches the order of accuracy required. Another consideration is the correction needed if the beam does not strike the target. Use of lasers will probably allow aiming correction by sensing reflected energy from the target, but in the case of particle beam weapons there is no reflection of the transmitted energy. This difficulty may be offset by the greater likely beamwidth of the particle beam but, even so, correct aiming may have to be confirmed by sensing of secondary radiation from the target.

KILL ASSESSMENT

Ignoring the complicating factor of discrimination between warheads and penetration aids, it is clearly necessary to avoid wasting weapons by targeting 'dead' warheads. This implies a requirement for kill assessment, the difficulty of which is dependent on the type of weapon employed and to some extent on which part of the missile trajectory it attacks. The use of KKWs should simplify that assessment as collision with a target at a closing velocity of several kilometres per second should cause it to explode or divert markedly from its necessarily accurate flightpath. Lasers and particle beam weapons might cause catastrophic and easily discernible kills but could also cause damage which is not detectable. Although structural damage or impaired electronics might render an RV unable to survive re-entry or to attack its allocated target, it may have to be engaged again because of the prevailing uncertainty. Even apparent break-up of a target could be a programmed action by the attacker as a form of deception with the first hint of interference. Thus it is likely that kill assessment could be straightforward in the boost and terminal phases but in the intermediate phases it may remain a serious problem. As a result consideration must be given to the scaling-up of weapon systems to achieve an unmistakable 'hard' kill. Estimates of the energy which would have to be delivered to differing target types to achieve hard kills can only be the product of a sound understanding of the damage mechanisms of DEWs. However, in the final analysis, it does seem that a more sensible goal for successful kill assessment would be more positive kills rather than more sophisticated assessment techniques.

BATTLE MANAGEMENT

The requirements for surveillance, discrimination, pointing and tracking, and kill assessment all point to the need for an overall management system to ensure that all or most of the threatening elements of attacking ballistic missiles are detected and defeated. Obviously, this control must be achieved in the most efficient manner to take advantage of the finite number of sensors and weapons and the limited power and fuel available. Many argue that battle management of an overall defence would be a much more difficult proposition than the provision of the other elements of the system's hardware. They may be right, because virtually every component could be tested in advance but not the integrated operation of the whole.

The task of battle management would be to provide functions for each defensive layer and also to link those layers. Each of them would need to acquire, track, discriminate, allocate weapons and evaluate success before passing its 'picture' and assessments to the succeeding layer. The overall management system must control the resources, delegate control to individual layers, coordinate the handover between layers, ensure the survival of the defensive system without compromising the main aim of defending the targets of the ballistic missiles, and provide the overall status to the human controllers. The software to control such an immense project would have to be much larger and more complex than any existing system. A US

Department of Defense Defensive Technologies Study Team estimated that over 10 million lines of computer code might be required for the BMD systems which they investigated. Moreover, not only would it be much larger but it would need to be significantly more fault-free or fault-tolerant than any earlier system. It is probable that automated computer programming techniques would be needed and, in the absence of realistic operational training, those programs would have to carry out self-checking reliability tests to eliminate design errors. Overall data processing would have to be distributed throughout the system to minimise the need for data transfer and to reduce the risk of loss of a single critical portion.

With the high dependence on computers and the very speed with which a ballistic missile attack could develop, strong reservations have been expressed for the ability to exert human control over such a complex network. Thus a wholly trustworthy command and control system would be an essential adjunct to battle management. Furthermore, in the absence of demonstrable and comprehensive testing and reliability of the entire system, there would have to be credible testing of sub-systems to provide confidence of its capability in war.

POWER IN SPACE

Space weapons in particular would demand high power supplies. Particle beams, lasers and EMRs would require many megawatts of electrical power. Currently, most satellites operate with supplies in the kilowatt range derived from solar energy. This method shows no promise of development to the scale needed and, therefore, it appears that nuclear and chemically produced energy must be developed. One challenge for space power sources will be reliability of operation after a prolonged period in space without routine and regular maintenance. The answer might be a nuclear source which could provide a steady, high power while chemical energy might provide the surge peak powers required for weapon firing. To this end the United States aims to conduct an experiment with a nuclear-powered electric generator designated SP-100 in the early 1990s. In this context it is worth noting that the Soviet Union has not been without problems with its nuclear-powered RORSATs.

COUNTERMEASURES

In describing the method of operation of each of the parts of a possible system to defend against a large-scale attack by ballistic missiles, it will be clear that the provision of a countermeasure to each and every part could be developed. In case that observation be thought to be an immediate undermining of such defences, it must be recorded that a number of those countermeasures bring their own penalties of expense and technical complexity to the attacker.

Most sensors would be designed to detect infra-red radiation and in most cases the detectors would have to be extremely sensitive to detect their targets. It is this very sensitivity which makes them vulnerable to 'blinding' by overloading the sensors at their narrow operating wavelengths. Sources of decoy energy at similar wavelengths could also prove troublesome. As there would be a number of sensors covering the threat spectrum the most effective blinding device might be a nuclear weapon. While its use could create difficulties for the remainder of the attacking

PLATE 12.9. Artist's impression of a space-based nuclear power source. (*US DoD*)

force by physical or radiation damage, it could be very effective against terminal radars and defences and would demand considerable hardening of the defender's own sensors and electronic equipments.

Decoys and penetration aids deployed in the post-boost phase would certainly create a complicating scenario for the defences by virtue of the number of objects. Thereafter, discrimination could be complicated not only by arranging for decoys to resemble RVs but also, if possible, by designing RVs to look like decoys. This simulation or deception might be created by shape, size or even by modification of temperature signatures. However, to defeat sophisticated discrimination techniques, the decoys would have to replicate faithfully all aspects of the RVs they are meant to represent. In this case it might be more sensible to increase the number of warheads rather than produce equally costly decoys. This option would only be available if existing ballistic missiles have the spare payload capacity, otherwise expensive new missiles would be needed.

The traditional military technique of increasing hardness or resistance to damage with the use of armour remains applicable to an era of space warfare, although straightforward armouring brings with it the penalty of weight and increased cost of launch. Nevertheless ablative coatings, which evaporate when heated and provide a protective shield for RVs on re-entry into the earth's atmosphere, could be applied elsewhere as a form of protection against laser damage. This measure would bring a serious weight penalty and in any case would not be effective against KKWs or particle beam weapons. The boosters themselves might be made less vulnerable by polishing or revolving them and so reduce the effectiveness of continuous wave lasers by effectively dispersing the laser energy over a larger surface area, but this defensive tactic could be overcome by the use of a pulsed laser or the employment of one of the other weapon types.

The defensive leverage obtained by successful attack in the boost phase could be reduced if the length of the boost phase could be shortened by the use of 'fast burn' missiles. Most current ballistic missiles burn for about 300 seconds but the United States' MX ICBM burns for only about half that time. If the boost phase could be shortened and the height at which it is completed can be markedly reduced, then not only is the period of this most vulnerable phase abbreviated but the attention of weapons which can only operate above the atmosphere could be avoided. With less success in the boost phase many more defensive weapons would be needed as RVs are deployed and target numbers proliferate. The attacker can aim to evade some or all of the defences described by employing ballistic missiles on depressed flightpaths within the atmosphere or by using totally different weapons like cruise missiles, aircraft or other air-breathing vehicles. Not only is the warning time of attack much reduced by use of such vehicles but another complementary set of air defences would have to be deployed. It is just this sort of threat which could face Western Europe and in this case, with warning of only a few minutes, defences are likely to depend much less on space-based equipment than does the SDI concept for defence of the United States.

The old adage that attack is the best means of defence could be applied to protection of the attacking ICBMs by attacking some or all of the components of the defences. For example, a defensive constellation could prove vulnerable to ASAT weapons. It could also be attacked by space weapons of the types already described which might have long been in space or launched as a precursor to the launch of its ballistic missiles. Thus the effectiveness of defences in the face of countermeasures will rely on an intelligent estimate of the potential adversary's capabilities during the development stage. Thereafter, they would have to be modified to keep at least abreast of the opponent's anticipated advances. A failure to do so could be disastrous as there could be little hope of quickly modifying equipment or changing tactics to meet an unexpected threat in time to be effective. For all those reasons a thorough analysis of the feasibility and possible vulnerability of a defensive system must be completed before its deployment can be considered.

CONCLUSION

This Chapter has described a number of options for strategic defence against attack by ballistic missiles. It has also touched on the complexities which face a nation trying to build such a defence. Defensive techniques range from the relatively mature chemical rockets to those of particle beam weapons which are barely beyond the concept stage. Other areas such as high-speed computers and the associated software for battle management will need years of further development. In the case of the United States, the SDI could founder for any of a number of reasons. The high material cost of fielding such a comprehensive and complex system must be weighed against the possible cost in human life of not doing so. Many of the techniques being considered may seem beyond comprehension to the layman and therefore may be considered not feasible. To counter that view it may be pertinent to quote a scientist who argued in 1932 that, 'There is not the slightest indication that nuclear energy will ever be obtainable. It would mean that the atom would have to be shattered at will'. That scientist was Albert Einstein! Even if the Initiative could prove feasible it might remain vulnerable to physical attack, decoy or deception. If cost, feasibility and vulnerability are not insuperable obstacles to deployment, there will still be the hurdles of public support and even political will in the United States for it to see the light of day.

A further influencing factor on the possible deployment of SDI could be the changing relationship between the United States and the Soviet Union which could make the provision of strategic defences unnecessary. Much could depend on the perception of the SDI by the Soviet Union and its reaction to the research, development and deployment. That reaction could take the form of bolstering its own defences and, by the admission of its own General Secretary, she is already researching all the technologies being pursued by the United States. Alternatively, it might choose to proliferate its strategic offensive weapons whether or not they are ballistic missiles. If the number of ICBMs were to be increased, however, this would ignore the unratified SALT limitation on such weapons. Nevertheless, the Soviet Union might feel justified in so doing because any deployment of ABM defences in space would contravene the ABM Treaty. Instead, it is to be hoped that both nations will recognise the destabilising influence of the unavoidably long deployment phase of any strategic defences. Such recognition would allow them to opt for lower levels of offensive weapons and thereby make those very defences unnecessary.

The Future

The Future

The authors of this book have tried to give a broad understanding of where the military powers stand today in the new dimension of space warfare. Individual chapters have also looked to the near future and identified the likely changes and improvements which may appear in due course. Some common themes connect these future forecasts, so it is fitting that the book should end by drawing together these threads to propose one possible list of future military space concerns.

13

The Future

Looking back over the remarkable advances made in space during the 33 years since Sputnik-1's launch, one could almost be excused for thinking that space operations had reached maturity and become an exact science. Military and civil systems are now carrying out a variety of operational tasks and have been performing well for many years. However, a moment's reflection raises questions as to the military viability of current systems, viz their survivability, self-protection, interoperability, processing capability, autonomy or versatility. Examination of each area leads to the conclusion that there is much room for improvement, particularly if one considers operating such satellites in a military threat environment.

Continuous R&D (Research and Development) efforts not only add new capabilities to military satellites but also such efforts must try to provide reliable counters to any threats faced by the satellites. Space operations differ from terrestrial operations in many ways. One important distinction is the very long time, in military terms, which is needed to replace a satellite if it becomes unusable, for whatever reason. Two further complicating factors are the immense cost of placing even the smallest payload in space and the very long time it takes to build and test a new satellite. So the future for military space systems will almost certainly follow the path of providing more capable payloads, hardened and well protected, with an emphasis on survivability and autonomous operations in times of all-out aggression. With such requirements in mind, let us now examine some areas where the crystal ball is least cloudy.

LAUNCH CAPABILITY

One of the prerequisites of assured access to space is that launchers are available and ready to go at extremely short notice. In 1986 the United States learned a very harsh military lesson when the grounding of the Shuttle fleet left it without its major military launch capability. Despite the resumption of the Shuttle flight programme in late 1988, the US Department of Defense has sensibly returned to unmanned ELVs as its major means of attaining orbit. Military payloads are getting larger and larger, so it follows that launchers will have to become more capable. Indeed, some of the SDI experiments require a lift capability outside the range of current operational ELVs. The future, in the West, will therefore see a return to the ELV and a dramatic increase in the lift capability of such systems.

The Soviet Union already has a suite of capable, operational ELVs which seem to flow from a production line with comparatively few problems. However, the

Soviet future plans also include very heavy launch capabilities and they will have to learn to cope with the problems of operating their manned shuttle fleet.

WIDENING THE ELECTROMAGNETIC WINDOW

The chapter on communication satellites explained why military communications in space will rely on higher and higher radio frequencies in the future, with technology, processing power and cost being as important in the design process as pure military requirements. EHF and laser transmission technologies in particular promise exciting future capabilities for military satellites. Also, the sensors of surveillance satellites will look in new frequency bands. Infra-red detection of air-breathing vehicles from space is still in the experimental stage and new ICBM launch detection satellites will concentrate more in the ultra violet frequencies. Radar surveillance is still in its comparative infancy and much effort will go into radar imaging of both stationary and moving targets. Such a broadening of the electromagnetic window, for both sensors and transmission links, dictates that the future is secure for signal processing engineers!

SECURING THE WINDOW

The vital communication links to military satellites must be very reliable, with little risk of either being monitored or jammed. Higher communicating frequencies allow greater bandwidths, which in turn allow more room for sophisticated coding techniques like spread-spectrum. Also, higher frequencies lead to narrower, more directional beams which are more difficult to intercept or jam. Extremely powerful but small computers will be used on board the satellites to perform complex tasks such as adaptive beam-forming or nulling to defeat enemy jammers.

SMART SATELLITES

For a military system to be of any real value, it must be reliable and robust. Individual satellites are fairly robust and, because of their great distance from Earth, may be difficult to physically shoot down. However, an entire constellation's overall operating performance may be degraded quite easily if its Earth-based control network is destroyed by enemy action. In a period of protracted hostility, the fixed Earth-based control networks must therefore be seen as major targets, so a degree of autonomy will have to be built into the satellites. For example, in response to this very threat, by the end of this century the Navsar GPS Block-2R satellites will be able to make range measurements off each other and carry out the work of the Ground Segment, updating their own knowledge of their errors. In the event that the Earth-based updates stop arriving, the satellites will take over the update task and maintain their full accuracy for up to six months. Similarly, the advent of adaptive antennas and autonomous processing will allow satellites to combat the effects of jamming without reference to ground control and to reroute signals around the constellation so that the messages will still arrive at their intended destination.

Autonomy will perhaps be taken to its ultimate conclusion with the fully operational SDI system. The reaction time to a full-scale first strike would be short, in fact too short for man to control fully the defensive might of the SDI system. It therefore follows that the system must be largely autonomous in operation. Of course this means many millions of lines of computer code will need to be distributed around the ground and space components of the system and all the code must be 100 per cent error-free; the very continued existence of the human race may depend on it being error-free! Experience with such gigantic programmes dictates that there will be errors, many of which would surface only with full testing. But, and it's a big but, the SDI system, by its very nature, can never be fully tested, so a new way of writing error-free programmes must be developed. Inevitably, such programmes will largely be written by machines—machines that have yet to be invented.

SATELLITE LIFETIMES

One area of major difference between the Eastern and Western methods of conducting space operations is revealed by the life of their respective spacecraft. Western military satellites have ever-increasing lifetimes; nowadays seven years is a good average design life, as in the case of GPS or Skynet. The planned lifetime will soon creep up to 10 years, as with DSCS III, and so it goes on. Such cost-effectiveness is to be applauded in the commercial field but there is perhaps an additional consideration which dictates that for military satellites the capability for speedy replacement may be as important as having the system on orbit in the first place. Quick reaction launch and replacement capabilities are very expensive and understandably hard to justify in peacetime and the West has little such capability. The Soviet Union, on the other hand, has for some time conducted space operations with many much shorter-life satellites. For example, the average life of the early Glonass satellites was only around four months, or one year for a Molniya. The Soviets have also demonstrated the ability to surge-launch when necessary. It will be interesting, in the future, to see whether the long- or short-life military satellite predominates, or whether both approaches continue as now. Of course, the way ahead may be a mixture of both approaches with the expensive long-lifetime satellites providing the backbone of a system, with cheaper, shorter-life yet very capable vehicles on standby for wartime replacement.

MAN IN SPACE

Space is one of the most inhospitable of environments for man. Military man's place in space for the near future could well therefore be as a controller for R&D activities which require some measurement, adjustment or participation for which a robot would be unsuitable. Once an individual technology matures, better its pursuit is left to the robotic machines in the cold empty void, allowing man to return to his natural environment. Undoubtedly, man will continue to explore space, just because of the challenge it represents, but it is unlikely that we shall see orbital space fighter pilots in the same way as we see them nearer to Earth. Frankly, there are easier and more efficient ways of doing the job, without people on board.

SPACE WEAPONS

Space weaponry will undergo a profound change over the next 20 years. Initially, however, there will almost certainly be a major effort to update the existing technologies for BMD. The United States is forging ahead with its new chemical rocket-powered missile interceptors under the SDI programme. Kinetic kill capability rather than warheads will come as a result of major steps in both homing and guidance technology. The Superpowers both appreciate the shortcomings of the old ASAT systems, so are moving into the new era of beam technology and orbiting KKWs. Research into these SDI-type technologies continues apace in both East and West. The main challenge will be to scale up the techniques demonstrated in laboratories to full operational size.

SUMMARY

Military space operations differ from Earth-bound operations in fewer ways than might be first imagined. Tried and tested military doctrines and the laws of physics remain true, even under zero gravity! Only the scale is unique: speeds of many kilometres per second are the standard; distances to the enemy may be many thousands of kilometres; timing errors for operations of only a few thousandths of a second may divide success and failure. Military man has always been impatient to exploit any new medium and space is no exception. Barely have operational systems been lifted from the drawing-board before more capable and more viable systems are promised by technological progress. Rugged, autonomous and highly capable systems are now planned for space as well as the terrestrial battlefield. A decisive battle has yet to be fought in space and no doubt man has much to learn on the subject of the military control of space. The start of the twenty-first century will see full military Space Command structures for the forces of East and West, with new and powerful weapon systems at their disposal. It is to be hoped that this will not herald the beginning of the end for civilisation but merely the end of the beginning of military space operations.

Self-Test Questions

Chapter 1   Introduction
1. Explain how the need for military space operations arose.

Chapter 2   Satellite Orbits
1. Why cannot a satellite speed up and remain at the same orbital height?
2. State Kepler's Laws.
3. Why does an easterly launch from Cape Canaveral result in a 28.5-degree inclined orbit?
4. What are the two major effects of the Earth's equatorial bulge on satellite orbits?
5. What is the shortest orbital period that can be sustained? Why?
6. How can a satellite moving at many kilometres per second appear to be stationary in the sky?

Chapter 3   Getting into Orbit
1. What is meant by the specific impulse (SI) of a rocket motor?
2. Why is it necessary to use multiple-staged launch vehicles for some payloads?
3. Could strap-on boosters be used instead of multiple staging?
4. What is the most energy-efficient way of transferring a spacecraft from one orbit to another?
5. Give some advantages of Shuttle over HOTOL, and vice versa.

Chapter 4   Space Treaties
1. Which treaty bans the use of nuclear weapons in space?
2. What were the main points of the Outer Space Treaty?
3. Would the building of anti-ballistic missile (ABM) defences along America's east coast contravene the ABM Treaty?
4. What is the 'hot-line' and what links does it use?

Chapter 5   Communication Satellites
1. Why cannot geostationary satellites communicate to the Earth's polar regions?
2. Why are the higher EHF frequencies attractive to military satellite communicators?
3. What is the major disadvantage of spin-stabilisation for a satellite?
4. What techniques can be used to minimise the effects of jammers on satellite communications?
5. Give at least three advantages which laser satellite communications will bring.

Chapter 6   Navigation Satellites

1. What are the disadvantages of 'Transit' for an airborne user?
2. How can a GPS user achieve such high accuracy without using an atomic clock in his equipment?
3. What is the main reason for the GPS and Glonass ground track patterns being designed to move slowly westward, rather than being ground-repeating?
4. How does differential GPS work?
5. What are the main differences between GPS and Glonass?

Chapter 7   Meteorological Satellites

1. What are the two main types of meteorological satellite?
2. What is atmospheric sounding?
3. Why does it take Meteosat 30 minutes to image the whole Earth?

Chapter 8   Surveillance From Space

1. Describe a typical optical surveillance orbit.
2. What sort of a payload would be put into a 98-degree inclined orbit, and why?
3. Conventional radars require more power than can be supplied from solar panels. How do current radar satellites get around this problem?
4. What are the trends in surveillance from space?

Chapter 9   Satellite-aided Search and Rescue

1. What is the principle of operation of the COSPAS/SARSAT system?
2. What is the main difference between the rescue service offered on 121.5 MHz and 406 MHz?

Chapter 10   Man in Space—Physiological Constraints

1. What are the main physiological effects on the human body of reducing the atmospheric pressure and density?
2. What are the main problems facing a space suit designer?
3. What long-term effects will cause problems for man on very long-duration space-flights?

Chapter 11   The Surveillance of Space

1. Why is it important for space nations to maintain a detailed catalogue of objects in space?
2. What types of sensor can be used to maintain a space catalogue?

Chapter 12   Space Warfare

1. What are the two main ASAT interception techniques?
2. What are the main drawbacks of using nuclear weapons in space?
3. What are the four phases of flight of an ICBM?
4. What new ABM technologies are best suited to counter each of the four phases of ICBM flight?
5. What do you consider to be the biggest problems in implementing the SDI programme as a whole?

Chapter 13   The Future

1. What do you consider will be the major changes in military satellite technology in the near future?
2. Why will autonomy be important in future systems?

Glossary

ABM	Anti-Ballistic Missile
ABM	Apogee Boost Motor
AFSATCOM	(US) Air Force Satellite Communications
AOA	Airborne Optical Adjunct
APT	Automatic Picture Transmission
ARPA	Advanced Projects Research Agency
ASAT	Anti-Satellite
AVHRR	Advanced Very High Resolution Radiometer
AWACS	Airborne Warning and Control System
BMD	Ballistic Missile Defence
BMEWS	Ballistic Missile Early Warning System
BSTS	Boost Surveillance and Tracking Satellite
C	Celsius
C/A Code	Coarse/Acquisition Code (GPS)
CDMA	Code Division Multiple Access
COSPAS	Russian language abbreviation of Space System for Search for Distressed Vessels
DARPA	(US) Defense Research Projects Agency
DEW	Directed Energy Weapons
DGPS	Differential GPS
DMSP	Defence Meteorological Satellite Programme
DSCS	Defence Satellite Communication System
DSP	Defence Support Program
ECCM	Electronic Counter-Countermeasures
EHF	Extremely High Frequency
EIRP	Effective Isotropic Radiated Power
ELINT	Electronic Intelligence
ELV	Expendible Launch Vehicle
EMR	Electromagnetic Railgun
EORSAT	ELINT Ocean Reconnaissance Satellite
ERIS	Exoatmospheric Re-entry Intercept Sub-system
ESA	European Space Agency
ET	External Tank
EVA	Extra Vehicular Activity
FEL	Free Electron Laser
FLAG	Flexible Lightweight Agile Guided (missile)
G	Gravitational Force

GEODSS	Ground-based Electro-optical Deep Space Surveillance System
GHz	Gigahertz
GOES	Geostationary Operational Environmental Satellite
GPS	Global Positioning System
HEDI	High Endoatmospheric Defence Interceptor
HOE	Homing Overlay Experiment
HOTOL	Horizontal Take-off and Landing
ICBM	Intercontinental Ballistic Missile
IDSCS	Initial Defence Satellite Communication System
INS	Inertial Navigation System
IUS	Inertial Upper Stage
kcal	Kilocalorie
kHz	Kilohertz
KKW	Kinetic Kill Weapon
kPa	Kilopascal
LUT	Local User Terminal (COSPAS/SARSAT)
LV	Launch Vehicle
MCC	Mission Coordination Centre (COSPAS/SARSAT)
METSATNET	Meteorological Satellite Network
MHV	Miniature Homing Vehicle
MHz	Megahertz
Milstar	Military Strategic Tactical and Relay
MLV	Medium Launch Vehicle
mmHg	Millimetres of Mercury
MMIC	Monolithic Microwave Integrated Circuit
MOD(PE)	(UK) Ministry of Defence Procurement Executive
MOTIF	Maui Optical Tracking and Identification Facility
NASA	National Aerospace and Space Administration
NATO	North Atlantic Treaty Organisation
NAVSPASUR	(US) Naval Space Surveillance System
NOAA	(US) National Oceanographic and Atmospheric Administration
NORAD	North American Air Defense Command
NUDET	Nuclear (explosion) Detection
OMS	Orbital Manoeuvring System
OMV	Orbital Manoeuvring Vehicle
OST	Outer Space Treaty
P Code	Precision Code (GPS)
Pa	Pascal
PLSS	Portable Life Support System
RAE	Royal Aerospace Establishment
RCC	Rescue Coordination Centre
R&D	Research and Development
RMA	Remote Manipulator Arm
RORSAT	Radar Ocean Reconnaissance Satellite
RV	Re-entry Vehicle
SAINT	Satellite Interceptor
SALT	Strategic Arms Limitation Treaty

SAM	Surface-to-Air Missile
	Search and Rescue; Synthetic Aperture Radar
SARSAT	Search & Rescue Aided Tracking
SCORE	Signal Communication by Orbiting Relay Equipment
SDI(O)	Strategic Defense Initiative (Organisation)
SDS	Satellite Data System
SGEMP	Systems Generated Electromagnetic Pulse
SHF	Super High Frequency
SI	Specific Impulse
SIGINT	Signals Intelligence
SLCSAT	Submarine Laser Communication Satellite
SPOT	Système Pour l'Observation de la Terre
SRB	Solid Rocket Booster
STS	Space Transportation System (US Shuttle)
TDMA	Time Division Multiple Access
TDRS	Tracking and Data Relay Satellite
TOVS	TIROS Operational Vertical Sounder
UHF	Ultra High Frequency
UN	United Nations
VAS	Visible Infra-Red Spin-Scan Radiometer Atmospheric Sounder
WGS 84	World Geodetic System of 1984

Bibliography

Aviation Medicine, editors J Ernsting, P F King; 'Manned Spaceflight' by R M Harding, Butterworths, 1988.

Aviation Week and Space Technology magazine, McGraw Hill Publications.

British Medical Journal, 'Aviation Medicine' (2nd Edition) by R M Harding and F J Mills, 1988.

Deep Black by William E Burrows, Bantam Press.

Foundations of Space Biology and Medicine, Editors M Calvin and O G Gazenko. A joint US/USSR publication in three volumes. Washington DC, NASA SP-374, 1975. Vol 1: *Space as a Habitat*; Vol 2: *Ecological and Psychological Bases of Space Biology and Medicine* (2 Books); Vol 3: *Space Medicine and Biotechnology*.

Guardians—Strategic Reconnaisance and Satellites by Curtis Peebles, Presidio Press.

Jane's Defence Weekly magazine, Jane's Information Group.

Jane's Spaceflight Directory 1988–89 edited by Reginald Turnill, Jane's Information Group.

New Scientist magazine.

Spaceflight magazine, The British Interplanetary Society.

Space Handbook, by US Air Command and Staff College, January 1985, Air University Press.

'Space Physiology and Medicine' by A E Nicogossian and J F Parker, Washington DC, NASA SP-477, 1982.

Soviet Space Programs 1976–80 US Senate Report by Committee on Commerce, Science and Transportation (Chairman the Hon Bob Packwood), December 1982.

The Soviet Year in Space, editions for 1985, 1986 and 1987, Teledyne Brown Engineering, USA.

Survival in Space: Medical Problems of Manned Spaceflight by R M Harding, Routledge, 1989.

Index

195